# CARING
## how to cope

*Janet Horwood*

**A practical guide**

A

## ACKNOWLEDGEMENT

I would like to thank all those who willingly gave time to read and comment on this book and to tell me of their experiences of caring. Special thanks to East Sussex Care for the Carers Council for so much up-to-date advice and information.

*To John, with love*

First published 1994.
© Janet Horwood, 1994

Health Education Authority
Hamilton House
Mabledon Place
London WC1H 9TX

ISBN 1 85448 923 2

Typeset by Type Generation Ltd
Printed and bound in Great Britain by
Biddles Ltd, Guildford and King's Lynn

# CONTENTS

# INTRODUCTION

Caring can be a very demanding job. If it were taken on by paid professionals it would probably call for the skills of several different people. Yet all over Britain men and women willingly take on the responsibility to care for a close relative or a friend.

Although the job has its rewards and many carers feel pride in what they do, there are also times when carers feel depressed, angry, frustrated, bored and tired out. This is when they need help. Yet so many carers never share the burden of care, or even their feelings, with anyone else. By reading this book, dipping into the chapters that interest you, you'll be able to take that first step towards getting the support and advice you need.

Knowing what's available, how to find out more and how to make the system work for you, will make it easier for you to stand up and ask for what you need. You can be in charge of the situation rather than ruled by it. You'll be able to make choices, maybe for the first time in years.

Help is still thin on the ground but the message to carers, often from other carers, remains the same: never be afraid to ask and keep asking. It may not be possible to get precisely the service you want but there are often alternatives.

Many carers feel that they lead very restricted lives, with little opportunity to develop or even keep up their own interests. That's why some parts of this book are just for you. To remind you that you do still exist as an individual and not just as a carer for someone else. If you can put yourself first occasionally, you'll be able to gather the emotional and physical resources you need to cope with caring in a way that's right for you and the person you care for.

This book is for people caring for an adult – whether it's a partner, spouse, parent or friend. Often carers simply don't have the time to gather information or think of ways round problems – this book will help you to do so. Those caring for children with special needs will need different information and help.

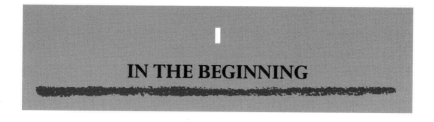

# IN THE BEGINNING

## Becoming a carer

*"It happened so gradually. I'd never thought of myself as a carer. I became one almost without noticing."*

*"The accident changed everything. There was no time to think. He's my husband and I still love him."*

*"We discussed it as a family first and felt that having my mother come to live with us was the best solution."*

*"The thought of either of my parents going into a home really upset me – but as an only child there was no alternative."*

*"At the time I felt reluctant but I was the only one who could do it. She'd brought me up, now it was my turn."*

*"I was put under some pressure by my brother and my mother's GP to look after her. We've managed but I still feel I was manipulated."*

There are so many different ways in which people start caring. For some it may be quite simply what they want to do, either out of love or because they feel they're the best person for the job. For many the feeling of duty is strong and they may care willingly but maybe feel they've not had any real choice.

There are also different levels of caring. The person you care for may be very ill or disabled or mentally frail, needing help with virtually everything from toileting to feeding. There may be many years of life ahead or just a few months. They may have a progressive condition such as dementia or a disability which needs more care as the months and years pass. You may be caring for your spouse, partner, parent, distant relative, neighbour or friend. – child

Carers are different too, ranging from young people still in their teens to mothers with young children, to men and women in their seventies and beyond.

There's a difference too between live-in carers (sharing accommodation with the person cared for), and live-out carers who may devote a few hours a week to shop, help with housework or just keep the person cared for company. For a live-in carer the demands on time may be much greater.

*"Sometimes I feel so exhausted I can't think straight. It's not her fault, it's the dementia that makes her so restless at nights and then, during the day, I constantly have to keep an eye on her. I never know what she might do while my back's turned."*

Live-out carers may also find themselves doing more than they expected:

*"I was doing the odd bit of shopping. Then I began cooking one or two meals. One day I realised that I was spending so much time there – helping her get up and dressed in the morning, making and giving her meals, getting her ready for bed at night. Suddenly I was spending more time looking after my mother than I was at home being a wife to Alan and mother to my three children."*

Through the different experiences of caring there is a common thread. Carers are ordinary men and women who are taking the responsibility to look after someone else. As a carer you may not have had any choice as to whether or not to take on this role but thinking about what is involved can help.

Obviously the best time to do this is at an early stage when you're likely to be less tired and in a stronger position to look at the situation and take action. But this may not always be possible. You may be reading this book having been a carer for many years. But it's never too late to re-assess – even quite simple things can make a difference, as this carer found:

*"It had all happened so quickly. I just had no time to think. Then I became my own worst enemy – convinced that I was the only one who could do the job. In the end it was my son who forced me to sit down and think it through. He made me see that it was possible to share the load and let go from time to time."*

Another carer, who wasn't married and whose mother, though in a wheelchair was still able to go out and about, created her own solution:

*"It was hard to find anyone to care for my mother and I didn't want to say goodbye to my social life, so when I went out I took her with me. At first people thought it strange but Mum's always been outgoing and she soon made friends of her own so we didn't spend all evening sitting with each other. It was the best decision I could have made. I was still having a life outside the house and my mother also found it stimulating."*

## If there's time to plan

Talking about your caring role can help you see more clearly what's best for you and the person you care for, both now and in the future. From there you can start finding out as much information as possible.

*"When my mother had a stroke she was first in hospital and then in a convalescent home. It was clear that she wasn't going to be able to look after herself without some help. To be honest I wasn't keen but the thought of her in a home made my stomach turn over. While she was convalescing I talked to anyone I could get hold of – my GP, her GP, family, friends, a social worker and, of course, her. We had time to get a few things set up and although I would have preferred not to have to take on this responsibility, the time I had to get organised took away the resentment."*

## Who to talk to

### THE FAMILY

A round-the-table discussion with the whole family means that although you may be the main carer, you'll have the chance to make it clear that you'll need some help and support from the family.

If the person cared for will be living with you then your spouse and children's views should be heard. This is also the time to establish ground rules about privacy, general behaviour and so on. And discuss any areas of possible friction.

## THE PERSON YOU'RE CARING FOR

If possible the person cared for should also be involved in some of the family discussions.

> *"Although my mother-in-law and I got on well and she was a wonderful grandma, she also had quite a strong personality. Before she came to live with us I plucked up the courage to have a very straight talk with her about interfering with the way I brought up the children. The children were also involved and promised to be considerate about noise, for instance. I think we all found it really hard to be so honest and I didn't want to hurt her. There were tears but it was worth it. It hasn't been plain sailing but I am sure it's been a lot easier."*

You also need to talk calmly to the person you'll be caring for to find out what they'd like. The sort of care you envisage may not be right for them. They may be determined, for instance, to continue to live alone or they may hate the idea of sharing your home. Try and consider what they may be feeling – anxiety about how things will work out, guilt at being a 'nuisance', loss of confidence because they're being looked after, loss of self-esteem and so on.

> *"My mother and I had always got on quite well but within weeks of coming to live with us she became so bad tempered and obstinate. I was at my wit's end. It was only a chance conversation with another carer that made me start giving her things to do around the house. She was far more settled after that. I realised that the obstinacy was her way of asserting herself."*

Sometimes it's not possible to have such discussions – the person may be too ill or too mentally frail. Then you must do what you think best and choose what's right for both of you in the circumstances. You may decide that you can't give the care needed yourself or that you may be able to give just some of it or for a certain time (see Chapter 9 for more advice on this).

## OTHER PEOPLE

If you're on your own, or are finding it hard to get family support, then talk to someone you like and trust. You should talk to your GP (or to the cared for person's GP if it seems appropriate) at this stage anyway and make sure that he/she knows that you are now a carer. You could also talk to a social worker or district nurse. Other carers may be able to help from their own experience, while a trained counsellor can help you sort out your feelings (see Chapter 2 for more about this).

If you have doubts about taking on, or continuing with your role as carer, you may prefer to talk to one of the above people first. They'll be able to tell you about the alternatives or they may suggest ways to make your job less of a burden and help you to carry on caring if this is what you want (see Chapter 9).

### Things to think about

◆ *Where is the caring to be done? If the person you care for is going to live with you, you'll need to think about a lot of things.*

◆ *Is your home suitable? Is there enough space, not just to offer a separate room, but also to accommodate any furniture the person may wish to bring? Will stairs be a problem? If so, are there alternatives (e.g. making a bedroom and bathroom downstairs)? Could you get a grant for this?*

◆ *Are there enough facilities, e.g. toilets, bathroom?*

◆ *Are there minor adaptations you could make to make life easier? E.g. building a ramp, better lighting on the stairs, installing a chair lift. (See Chapters 5 and 6 for suggestions and how you get help to pay for these things.)*

◆ *How will having an extra person in the house affect your life and the life of your family? For instance, do you normally get on well with the person, or is there friction? Can this be sorted out, say, by talking it over or getting an objective outsider to broach the subject?*

◆ *Will they have a part to play in family life? It can be just as hard for a person to lose their privacy as it is for you to make changes to accommodate them into your life.*

*"I'd been a volunteer helper in an old people's home and it'd always struck me how quickly some people deteriorated when they had nothing to do but sit around all day waiting for the next meal. When my father moved in with us, although he couldn't get around easily, I made sure he had things to do. He listened to his grandchildren reading, helped prepare meals and so on. It helped him feel useful – and he was – he wasn't just an old man needing care."*

- *Would it be easier to travel to give the care needed? Would this give you more time for yourself? Would the other person be happier staying in familiar surroundings? If moving house is an option, think very carefully about taking an older person away from a familiar environment and well-loved friends. Maybe there are other ways, other solutions to consider first. Because these things often take time to organise, it would be worth having a trial period away from home before irrevocable steps (like selling the house) are taken.*
- *Are you thinking of moving into the home of the person you care for? Chapter 7 looks at your housing rights and what this can mean to you in the future.*
- *How much care is needed? Talk to the GP, consultant, district nurse or social worker and ask them to explain exactly what's needed. You can then decide whether you're going to do this alone – maybe you're just needed to help with shopping and the occasional outing – or with help from others (e.g. family members) if the care needed is more comprehensive. If you're a woman, your husband and children may not be able to help your mother use the toilet or get dressed but they can give you a breather by taking her to the shops or sitting with her some afternoons or evenings.*
- *Community care means that local authority social services departments are now responsible for assessing the needs and arranging appropriate care for people needing help. In some places carers' support is good but elsewhere, in rural areas or in districts where money is short, carers have to manage with very little formal support.*
- *Even in the better areas, services are patchy but Chapter 4 tells you about the support systems available and how to make the most of them. Assessments of needs take a while so you may find you're having to cope in the meantime.*
- *Will you need trained or professional help? Now's the time to discuss this with professionals like a GP or social worker. It's also the time to be prepared to ask and keep asking for what you want (see Chapter 4).*
- *Has the person you care for got a specific illness or disability – for instance, Alzheimer's or Parkinson's Disease, a stroke, arthritis, diabetes? You need to find out as much as you can and what to expect, both now and in the future. The more you know about*

managing the illness and its treatment, the more at ease you'll feel. The person you care for will also be more relaxed. Your GP may be helpful or you could talk to the specialist or consultant.

♦ Some doctors do seem to have a talent for the obscure and much information will be general rather than specific but don't be afraid to persevere. Take a list of questions with you, write down the answers and ask for more explanations if you don't understand the first time.

♦ There are national associations for most illnesses and disabilities and they can be a wonderful source of clear, concise information (addresses for the main ones are included at the back of the book). They may also be able to put you in touch with a local support group.

♦ If you're caring for someone who's ill and has only a short time to live, or if the information about the illness or disability is particularly distressing, then you may like to consider counselling and guidance (see Chapter 8).

- *What about money? The benefits that carers can claim in their own right is very low. Invalid Care Allowance, for instance, is only paid to a fifth of those caring full-time and you can't claim it once you're over 65. If caring means giving up paid work you need to assess what this could mean to you in the long-term, e.g. loss of pension rights, savings, the extra costs involved, etc. (see Chapter 7).*
- *Many carers are very badly off financially and that means that if statutory services are not available they can't even afford to pay for it. See Chapter 5 to ensure that you and the person you care for are getting all the benefits and allowances, and Chapter 7 for ways to handle personal finances.*
- *How fit are you? The healthier you are, the better you'll manage. If you have any health worries or if taking on caring could make a condition (like a bad back) worse, then seek help now (see Chapter 3 for ways to improve and maintain your health).*
- *What about the future? What will happen as you get older particularly if the person you care for needs more care? How will you manage? Now's the time to plan for regular breaks and extra help.*

**"Right from the start, I knew it would only work if I had regular breaks. But mum really resented it if I went out – even for an hour to do some shopping. It was three years before I had the courage to organise things so that I could have a week's holiday. I didn't feel happy about it but it broke the ice and she accepts it now."**

## When there's no time to plan

In an emergency, or when the need for care has crept upon you, or if someone you love dearly needs you, there seems to be little time to think. Try to find time to talk to as many people as possible: health professionals, like your GP; friends and other carers too. It will help you get a perspective. But there are questions you can ask yourself. This isn't selfish, it's sensible. You have an important job to do and to do it well you have to consider yourself.

**You could ask yourself the following questions**
- *Why am I taking this on?*
- *Do I really want to do this?*

- *What long-term effect will this have – on me and on my family?*
- *If I have doubts but still feel I should do something, how much can I offer to do?*
- *If I really don't want to do this what are the alternatives? (See Chapter 9.)*
- *What sort of things would make life easier for me as a carer?*
- *Who could I share this job with?*

## Coming out of hospital

Hospitals aren't supposed to discharge patients without ensuring that they're going to be adequately cared for. Some hospitals have a liaison nurse who starts planning for the patient's discharge from the moment he or she comes into hospital by co-ordinating the various services needed and following them up in the community. In other areas such services are not yet available. Some hospitals do provide relief bed services. This could give you the extra time you need.

Here are some questions to think about and ask before the person is discharged. The best person to talk to will vary from hospital to hospital. You could start by talking to the ward sister as she will be able to point you in the right direction. Hospitals generally have a social worker or a patient advocate, who can advise both patient and relatives or carers. Both are useful people to approach.

- *Has the hospital consulted you if you are to be the carer? If not, have a word with the ward sister. If you've been contacted make sure you get the name of the right person to talk to in future.*
- *Have you been given enough information about the illness or disability and the amount of care needed, e.g. about medication, lifting and so on? The consultant and/or ward sister should help here and, on arrival home, the GP or practice/district nurse.*

# Coming out of hospital *continued*

- *Has anyone checked that the home (either yours or the patients') is properly equipped? For instance, if the person can't manage stairs, is there a downstairs toilet? If not, you may need to ask about being lent a commode and other equipment. Talk to the hospital occupational therapist about this.*
- *Have you been given information on the support available in the community (either professional or voluntary) and any idea about what sort of respite care is available? The hospital social worker should have this information and be able to give you the relevant names and phone numbers.*

## Who can help now?

You might find these organisations useful. Their addresses are in Chapter 10, along with those specifically for different illnesses and disabilities. Carers National Association; Help the Aged; British Association for Counselling; Counselling Information Scotland; Age Concern; Social Services (see page 52).

# 2
# YOUR FEELINGS

As a carer there will be times when the closeness between you and the person you care for can make you feel good about yourself and what you're doing. A hug, a smile, a word of praise, a gesture or having time to talk honestly to each other can make such a difference. You may also have good feelings when you talk to other carers, when you share experiences, when you receive words of encouragement. These positive moments may help you through the really tough times.

But carers can have many painful feelings to deal with. Some of the things which cause these feelings can't be changed – for instance, the sadness when someone is ill or the sense of loss when a loved one's mind gradually becomes confused.

There are other, often stronger feelings, that you'll try and ignore because you're simply too exhausted, or you feel there's not much you can do to change things.

There can be resentment when all attention is focused on the person you care for, particularly if that person is very ill or disabled. Doctors, nurses, social workers may come to see you, they may talk to you but not about you. You get the feeling no one cares. It's easy, as time goes by, to reinforce this by overlooking your needs, putting yourself further and further into the background.

But you're still a person in your own right, doing a valuable job, often in difficult circumstances. Some parts of the country may have excellent support services for carers. Paid workers, such as social and health workers, work alongside them and they feel valued for what they do. Sadly elsewhere, especially in country areas, this support can be almost non-existent and then you have to draw on your own inner strengths to keep going. It may be hard to keep reminding yourself of your own worth.

*"I cry myself to sleep most nights and hope that the next day will be better. It never is but there's no point dwelling on it, is there?"*

But before you get to this stage it may help to know that you can do something, it doesn't have to be like this.

*"Looking back, I did spend a lot of time denying that I was so angry and resentful. I'd been effectively forced to care for my mother-in-law. In the beginning I took a deep breath and thought it'd be alright but as the months went by, I could feel this anger building inside. When I finally admitted to myself how I felt, I was shocked but then I could see why. After that somehow it was easier to get help, to talk to someone and sort things out."*

You may also be dealing with the emotional problems of the person you care for.

*"After the stroke my husband went to pieces. He wasn't that badly disabled but he convinced himself that his life was over. Every day he complained of being of no further use. I exhausted myself trying to make him see there was still a point in being alive. His sixtieth birthday was the turning point. I organised a huge surprise party, inviting all his friends past and present. It made him feel wanted, a special person. He laughed for the first time in months. It gave him the kick start he needed."*

# Recognising your feelings

Try to hold on to the good feelings you have about caring: pride in doing a good job; love for the person you care for; happiness on the days that are easier than others. It helps if you can share them with friends, other carers, the person you care for.

> *"Each day I give her a big hug and kiss and say, 'I love you'. She doesn't really know who I am now, but I can see in her eyes that it makes her feel good and it helps me to keep going."*

### THINKING OF YOUR NEEDS

> *"Somehow, as the days and months go by, you sort of cease to exist. Your whole life is so bound up in the needs of someone else. In the end I made a deliberate decision not to think about myself, not to care if I didn't go out or have time for myself. If I thought about it I felt worse and I convinced myself that nothing could be done anyway."*

We all have rights and one of the more important personal ones is to have some time for ourselves – some physical and emotional space – time when we can choose to be alone or with friends, time to have fun, time simply to think.

Because caring is physically and emotionally draining, your needs are usually the first thing to go out of the window. But they don't disappear, they're still there and that's when you can feel frustrated or resentful – and then guilty. If this has happened then you'll perhaps want to start quite slowly to put yourself first and get used to this and not feel bad about it.

### CARERS FIND IT HARD TO ASK FOR HELP

You may not think you need help. You may be too tired to bother. You may not know where to go to get this help (Chapter 4 will help). Many carers don't realise that they are carers and qualify for support of some kind. If you can get over this hurdle you've taken the first big step towards being stronger and recognising your needs.

Sometimes your request may be refused. This may already have happened to you and forced you back into your protective shell of coping alone. Try to be persistent – ask again, ask other people, make your voice heard. Strengthen yourself with some of the following:

## EACH DAY MAKE TIME AT HOME JUST FOR YOURSELF

Something simple, like a deep, relaxing bath; getting up a little earlier to have a quiet breakfast and read the newspapers or a magazine; watching a favourite TV programme; reading a book.

## TAKE UP A HOBBY

If it's hard for you to commit yourself to classes, many things can be studied at home by correspondence, including crafts. Or you can use books or television.

## HAVING PROBLEMS SLEEPING?

There's advice on insomnia in Chapter 3. But if your sleep is disturbed by the person you care for, then tell the support services who might be able to help. Night care is hard to get and you may be offered respite during the day. If so, use this time to catch up on lost sleep rather than housework. Family or friends can be asked to give you a night off, or to come in during the day so that you can put your feet up. In the meantime, snatch times when you can rest during the day – maybe when the person you care for is resting. Instead of doing the ironing, you can rest too.

## DON'T BE A PERFECTIONIST

Especially about housework: you can leave the chores once in a while without the whole world falling apart.

## SHARE YOUR FEELINGS

You may hesitate. You may feel it's a sign of weakness. It isn't. Talking about your feelings of despair, concern, fear or anger can help you understand them. The earlier you do it, the better. You may feel it's disloyal to talk about the person you care for, but talking with other carers, for instance, will often help you see that this isn't so. You can still love and respect the person you care for while talking about the things that annoy you:

> *"The weekly meetings of our carers' support group have been a lifeline. Hearing others talk about their feelings encouraged me to speak up and although it didn't change the situation at home, I felt as if some of the burden was lifted. We could laugh too about things that happened and that was such a relief."*

Your GP or social services will have contact names for your nearest carers' group or you could try the Carers National Association or Age Concern. If you prefer you could talk to a trained counsellor, an objective outsider who's there just for you, who you can talk to in confidence and who should be able to help you see things more clearly. Again, your GP should be able to put you in touch with a counsellor or you should contact the British Association for Counselling or the Westminster Pastoral Foundation for general information and advice on finding a local counsellor.

You may recognise some of these thoughts:

## I FEEL GUILTY BECAUSE...

*• I haven't done enough • I resent having to be a carer • I don't like/love the person I care for • I've lost my temper/been unkind to the person I care for • I feel trapped • I want to stop caring*

## I FEEL LONELY BECAUSE...

*• I've lost contact with friends and/or family • No one comes to see us any more • I never get out of the house*

## I FEEL DEPRESSED BECAUSE...

*• No one takes any notice of me • It's a never-ending grind, day after day with no end in sight • The person I care for will never get better and will probably get worse • I can't see the point of what I'm doing*

**I FEEL AFRAID BECAUSE...**
> • *I don't know what will happen in the future* • *What will happen if I fall ill?*

**I FEEL ANGRY BECAUSE...**
> • *I am coping alone and no one gives a damn* • *I don't get along with the person I care for* • *I hate what the person has become* • *I have been forced to do this job* • *The person I care for treats me badly*

There are ways to deal with these feelings. Some will be right for you, others won't. Equally, some of the thoughts you will have recognised, while others seem alien. The important thing for you is to choose solutions that you feel comfortable about.

## Handling the guilt

Guilt can be quite an overwhelming feeling because it makes you feel so bad about yourself. Like anger, it's the sort of feeling that you've probably been brought up to consider as 'wrong'.

> *"I kept thinking 'I shouldn't feel like this.' But the more I thought it, the worse it became. In the end, a friend suggested I saw a counsellor. Although I didn't really want to go, it did help in the end because it made me see things more clearly."*

Feeling guilty is often linked to the fact that you feel, rightly or wrongly, that you haven't done well enough, that there are people who disapprove of you. If you aren't getting on well with the person you care for, feel impatient and annoyed but feel you shouldn't have these reactions, that's where guilt comes in.

Only you will know the best solution but it may be that if you do feel resentful or if the relationship between you and the person you care for has got worse (or even if it's always been poor), you may need to make changes in the way you care.

## Think about the following:

### GETTING MORE BREAKS FROM CARING

You may want to think about the sort of support that could allow you to have a proper holiday for the first time in years or a break of two or three days every so often.

### STOPPING CARING

This could either be for a while or for good. There's more information about this in Chapter 9. If you think that no longer being a carer will make you feel even more guilty, discuss this with someone you trust. You may simply need someone to help you see that this is the right decision – or both of you. Or you may be able to compromise and organise a lot more support to take some of the pressure off.

> *"It took a lot to convince me that many of the problems were because I was doing too much – and resenting it. It wasn't easy to get the extra help but I asked everywhere – friends, voluntary groups and so on. In the end there were several people who came in and allowed me to have breaks and it did make a difference."*

If you have been unkind to the person you care for or abused them (either verbally or physically) then you need more support. Talk to your social worker, carers' group or GP. Or contact your local branch of Age Concern.

## Overcoming loneliness

Many carers feel isolated without quite realising how it happened. The longer you're cut off from the outside world, the harder it is to take that first step back into society.

> *"In the beginning I used to get out two or three times a week and Mum was fine on her own. Now though, I daren't leave her in case she has an accident or wanders off. The other day I realised I hadn't been out alone of an evening for over a year."*

This loss of contact with friends can be a problem, here are some ways of overcoming it:

◆ *If it's hard to get away then you could invite people to your house.*

*"I'd always been keen on knitting but once I started looking after Mum I lost interest. Then I saw a notice asking for blankets for Africa and I thought it would be a good idea to invite friends round so that we could knit squares together. It also solved my problem of getting out so rarely. We have now knitted several blankets and I really look forward to the weekly gathering."*

◆ *If the person you care for is unsociable or difficult, you may be able to arrange a break of an hour or two to allow you to go out and meet a friend for coffee. Or you could arrange for him / her to go out so that you have the house to yourself for a while to entertain your friends. Making the event a regular one will give you something to plan for and look forward to.*

◆ *Even if you haven't the will or energy to go out, try to make the effort – it really is worth it. Start small and don't expect too much.*

*"What saved me from real loneliness was talking to other people. In shops I'd make a point of chatting to the girl on the till, when the postman came I'd watch out for him – that'd be another few words. It was just contact with other people I needed."*

◆ *Use the phone. Even if you can't get out easily to meet people, you can keep in touch by phoning.*

◆ *Write letters. It's really nice to get a letter from a friend. It may also be easier to express what you feel in writing. If you have few friends or relatives to write to then you could join a penfriend club.*

◆ *If you belong to a religious group of any kind, you'll know there's more to organised religion than worship at the church, synagogue, temple or mosque. A religious group can be a wonderful source of comfort and support. If you have rejected religion in the past maybe it now has something to offer. You may gain comfort from talking to a priest or joining a bible discussion group.*

## Dealing with depression

*"It gets you down and it wears you down. Sometimes you want to go out and have a laugh but you've always got to do something for her. You've never finished the job"*

Depression takes many forms and has different symptoms. Here are some of the better known signs. You may have one or two or all of them.

◆ *not sleeping*
◆ *loss of appetite or eating more than usual*
◆ *lack of energy / constantly feeling tired*
◆ *crying easily or easily upset*
◆ *no longer wanting to do things you used to enjoy*
◆ *feelings of hopelessness / and feeling 'what's the point?'*
◆ *irritability or feeling agitated*
◆ *physical symptoms like headaches, shooting pains in the face and neck*
◆ *mood swings – feeling unhappy one week and totally elated the next.*

Depression is usually triggered by your circumstances but if one or more of the above symptoms has persisted for more than a month or so, you should go to your GP. Depression is a treatable condition.

# What your GP may suggest

**Anti-depressant drugs** can help relieve symptoms of depression – and if you've felt low for over a month your GP may prescribe them. They need about six weeks to take effect so you have to be patient. Also, one kind may not suit you but there are many to choose from.

**Tranquillisers** may be offered as a way of helping you to calm down and get a good night's sleep. These are addictive and so should be used with care. They can help you through a bad patch but are not a long-term solution. Avoiding tea, coffee, cola and cigarettes can help you sleep better as they're all stimulants.

**Counselling or other help** Your GP may suggest you see a counsellor or psychiatrist. There's no shame in this, no reason to be angry with yourself for feeling depressed or to regard it as weak or self indulgent. Drugs will help you cope but they will not solve underlying problems and anxieties.

> *"I'd been depressed for a couple of months before I saw my GP. I didn't want to take drugs and he agreed that tranquillisers weren't the answer. He did give me some anti-depressants and to my amazement they did help. I took them for about three months and they just helped me cope a bit better."*

Depression is often a sign that you have stopped caring for yourself. Think about some of these ideas:

◆ *Try to keep to a routine. Get up at the usual time, get dressed and go out, if possible, each day.*

◆ *Massage of any kind, but particularly aromatherapy, with sweet scented oils, soothes and relaxes. Having someone touch you makes you feel special. Reflexology – where the massage is concentrated on the feet – is an alternative. Both are very effective at relieving stress symptoms like headaches and insomnia. If money is a problem, some GPs refer patients for this sort of therapy and a qualified therapist may reduce the fee.*

◆ *Try not to turn down help if it's offered. You may have quite strong negative feelings about it such as: it's too little, too late; it isn't the sort of help I want or need (e.g. being offered half a day respite care when you really need two or three days); the person I care for would object to being left.*

◆ *As you begin to say no, remember that anything that can give you a breathing space will allow you to build your strength up to ask for more next time. Don't let your depression lure you into thinking you don't deserve help and support – you do.*

**"I was lucky to have a couple of good friends who wouldn't take no for an answer. They kept asking me to meet them for coffee, go to a film, a walk. I kept saying no and they kept asking. One day I somehow found myself saying yes. The next time it was easier to agree to go out and slowly I emerged into the sunlight again."**

## Acknowledging your fears

Carers are sometimes afraid – you may worry about money (see Chapters 5 and 7 for advice and information) or about illness.

Of course carers do fall ill and there may be times when you are just too unwell to continue your caring role.

**WHAT TO DO**

If you are ill, contact your GP as she or he will be able to advise and start to set in motion emergency support.

What is provided will depend on the circumstances and the needs of the person you care for. Respite care in a residential home or hospital may be appropriate or it may be possible for a whole range of services to be set up that will allow the person you care for to remain in his or her own home. (See Chapter 9 for more on what to do when you stop caring.)

Carers also worry about what will happen if they die before the person they care for. If this is a serious concern of yours then it is well worth discussing with those who support and help at the moment. Knowing that things will be taken care of if you are no longer there can relieve a lot of tension and worry.

## Allowing yourself to be angry

Carers often suppress their anger – they're afraid of what might happen if they let go.

> **"Some days the constant whining and carping drove me mad. I'd shout and scream at her, slam doors, threaten to leave her to look after herself. When I calmed down I felt so ashamed. It wasn't her fault really."**

It's natural to feel angry and irritable sometimes but many carers will feel they're being pushed to the limit day after day. Then you'll want to let fly – scream, shout or throw something. Mostly you'll resist but there are times when the anger and frustration have built up and can no longer be held back. Then there's a risk that you may abuse the person you care for, maybe verbally – threatening to put them in a home, calling them insulting names – or physically by shaking them, hitting them, depriving them of things like food, or refusing to dress them or take them to the toilet. Of course, it's against the law to abuse someone in this way. If this happens or you feel it might, it's important to seek help quickly. Talk to your GP, social worker or local support group. People will understand that you need more help or maybe that the time has come for you to do your caring in a different way. Age Concern have a factsheet on elder abuse which you might find helpful, because even if you're not looking after an old person the feelings are similar.

**If you feel irritated and angry you could try:**

- *Taking several deep breaths or leaving the room while you recover.*
- *Laughing it off and not taking it personally or seriously.*
- *Putting your energies into something physical – scrubbing the kitchen floor really hard, hitting a cushion or screaming (with the door shut and into a pillow).*
- *Talking to someone. Just having someone to tell about the particular incident or the things about the person you care for that really irritate you, can diffuse the situation.*

**"The first time I heard someone at the carers' group joking and laughing about something her Dad had done that drove her mad, I was quite shocked. In fact it's a good way to get things out of your system. Now I know there's somewhere to go and say, "Do you know what he did yesterday...?" and we have a good laugh together."**

# Other ways to cope

### MAKING LISTS

To help you feel better about yourself, you could make a list of all the things you do for the person you care for. Look at the list on the days when you feel low – it can reassure you to know that you do these things well.

List the things you enjoy about caring – feeling wanted, knowing you're doing an important job, still having the person you love with you, and so on. It can also help to list the less positive things – there will be some there that you can take action on.

### CHANGING YOUR ROUTINE

Some people like routine – it makes them feel secure to know that meals are always at certain times and that on Sundays they always go for a drive – but it can drive a carer mad! Small changes that don't upset the person you care for, can make all the difference and stop each week slipping into the next with no change.

**You could try:**

- *Getting up earlier a few mornings a week.*
- *Buying a different newspaper or magazine.*
- *If you always see the same group of friends, go out of your way to make new contacts.*
- *One carer, whose mother was physically badly disabled but mentally alert, found a way of livening up her week by suggesting that her mother might like to visit old people in a local residential home.*

**"Mum loved the idea. Although she was dependent on me for so much she could still offer something to others. It broke the week for her to get out of the house as well as giving me time to myself. And of course the people at the home enjoyed Mum's visits."**

# Stand up for yourself

It can be easy to feel you're being taken advantage of — by family, friends and by the support services. Members of your family who could have taken on this job may be heaving sighs of relief that they escaped, while the support services, under-funded and under-resourced, will also be glad that you're there.

You may find that people compliment you on how well you're doing but instead of feeling pleased you simply feel angry or depressed. Family and friends who say, admiringly, "I don't know how you cope", or helplessly, "I wish there were something I could do", aren't offering you any support at all.

You may feel better and stronger if you respond with, "Yes, I do manage but I could do with more help. Could you look after Dad for a couple of hours this week?" You can use the same approach with the support services.

**Remember**
Don't be afraid to ask for what you want. Here are three rules to help you:

- *Make a decision about what you want.*
- *Ask yourself if it's reasonable.*
- *If it is, ask for it straightforwardly.*

Classes in assertion training are quite common these days. Ask at your local adult education college. If there's nothing on offer, or it's hard to get out, the Open University has courses and there are several good books on the subject including Anne Dickson's book *A Woman In Your Own Right*.

# Be informed

Most carers find getting information the hardest job of all. You may also be too tired to bother.

♦ *This book will help by telling you what's available and whom to approach (see Chapters 4, 5, 6 and 7). It will help you to understand how much stronger you'll feel when you have some knowledge, and that it is worth picking up the phone or writing that letter.*
♦ *Armed with information you will be better able to deal with the support services and will be clearer in your mind about what your needs (and those of the person you care for) are.*
♦ *Find out as much as you can about your dependent's condition – sometimes this will be painful but you will have some idea of what the future holds.*

# Be realistic

Carers often set themselves such high goals. You want to do the best you can, but you're not superhuman, so accepting help isn't a sign of failure. It simply gives you a chance to gather your forces and do your bit of the caring really well.

# Learn to relax

There are many things you can do to relax. Choose the one that suits you. You can buy cassettes of soothing waves, music and voices. You may like to have a religious element. There are also courses on meditation to go to. Yoga, as well as providing the stretching to strengthen your muscles, incorporates valuable relaxation and meditation techniques.

♦ *You can practise relaxation at home. You will need an uninterrupted half-hour. For many carers this may only be possible at night or first thing in the morning.*
♦ *Wear comfortable, loose-fitting clothes. Make sure you're warm. Have low lighting or maybe candles.*
♦ *Lie on your back either on the bed or on the floor on a blanket.*

◆ *Take several slow, deep breaths in through the nose and out through the mouth. Then try and make the breaths even slower and deeper. Finally, breathe in, hold the breath to a count of three, and breathe out. Repeat three times.*

◆ *Now work round your body, tensing then relaxing. Start with the hands, then arms and shoulders, taking each side in turn. Move on to the feet and legs and up until you reach your head. Screw up your face and then let it flop – lips apart, jaw hanging loose. Rest like this for about 15 minutes, aware of the heaviness in your whole body. If you're very tired you may fall asleep. Don't worry, this is normal. When the relaxation period is over, get up slowly and calmly to avoid feeling giddy.*

◆ *You could try meditation. Meditation works well for all sorts of people – even, to their surprise, for those who start off thinking it's a bit of a joke. You need to concentrate on something to clear your mind of all the usual, everyday thoughts. It could be a soothing word or sentence. Or an object, say, a flower or candle. Sit in a comfortable chair or lie in your relaxed position. Spend 15 to 20 minutes repeating the words or concentrating on the object. Ignore all distracting thoughts – just let them come and go.*

◆ *If you can organise a break for yourself, for a day or a weekend, a retreat (even if you aren't religious) can offer you a chance to switch off. You can organise a personal retreat or go on something more organised. Many retreats also have someone to whom you can talk about your life and concerns.*

## Understanding relationships

Caring can alter a relationship. Sometimes it can bring you closer, other times it can cause a rift. For the person being cared for there may be many concerns – about being a nuisance, annoyance at being dependent, or fear of the future.

**"My father's such an even-tempered man but within weeks of coming to live with us he was making my life impossible. We seemed to constantly be at loggerheads over quite minor things and he was so obstinate. In the end we talked and although he didn't say anything directly I realised that this was all part of him trying to cling onto his independence."**

If this is a situation you recognise then talking is the simplest answer — preferably with the person you care for. It may not be possible or it may be too painful. A trusted family member or friend, a counsellor or social worker is a good alternative. If things are very tense it may be easier for an outsider to help by talking things over with you, either together or separately.

As a child caring for a parent you do have to come to terms with the change in roles. This can be hard especially if the relationship was never particularly close or loving. This is an area which carers can find most distressing.

*"I look after my mother because it's my duty — after all she looked after me. But she's always criticising me — my cooking, the way I bring up the children, the fact that I go out occasionally — it really gets to me some days and I want to scream at her, 'Well, if you don't like it here go into a home,' but I know I can't do that to her, whatever I feel."*

If you're a young carer having to look after a parent when, a few years ago, that parent looked after you, the feelings of embarrassment, resentment, fear of not being able to manage can be even stronger.

Talking to a counsellor about the relationship will help you to put things in a broader context — you may be able to understand why the closeness isn't there.

On a day-to-day basis, you may find it easier to cope if you try not to let things get to you, if you avoid confrontations over small issues and take advantage of times when your parent is in a better mood. Friends and support groups can be helpful too as places where you can unload your frustration.

Caring for a partner raises other problems — you may well have promised to care for each other in sickness and in health but the sort of care some partners provide 24 hours a day, year after year, demands a great deal of them. Once you stood side-by-side as equals, now the balance has shifted. It will be painful not to be able to share many things that held you close. A disability may mean you can no longer go for long walks together, dementia can put a stop to your social life, a stroke sufferer may have impaired speech which makes ordinary conversation impossible. The attitude of your partner can also make a difference.

> *"I found it hard to keep my patience with Geoff. I knew it was hard for him to be in a wheelchair when he'd been so active but all he did was moan about what he couldn't do, refusing to see that there were still other things he could do."*

You may have to be inventive to find things that make the person you care for feel wanted and important. Geoff's wife found the answer by spending some time listing areas in which she needed help and from them, finding the things that were important that she knew Geoff could do.

> *"Geoff's an organised sort of person – quite unlike me, so I handed all the bills and finances over to him and he got real pleasure out of getting a system going."*

It's also important to continue to touch, hold, kiss and cuddle. Physical closeness – hugging, a loving squeeze as you go past, means a great deal and can relieve many tensions.

## Sexual relationships

When you're caring for a partner your sexual feelings may change. You may no longer desire them or their illness may mean that emotionally or physically they change. As a carer, making love will be the last thing you may want as you fall into bed at the end of an exhausting day.

### TALK ABOUT ANY PROBLEMS IF YOU CAN

Talk first between yourselves and then maybe with your GP. For instance many drugs have side effects (amongst them impotence) and your GP may be able to help or explain this. Counsellors can help with relationship problems of all kinds.

**IF YOUR PARTNER HAS A SPECIFIC ILLNESS**

If this is the case then the voluntary organisation which supports them may also be able to advise (see Chapter 10 for addresses).

**FOR SEXUAL PROBLEMS**

If you have a sexual problem which arises from a physical disability you can contact the Association to Aid the Sexual and Personal Relationships of People with a Disability (SPOD).

# Keeping the family together

Not all carers are lone people caring for one person in a vacuum. Husbands, wives, partners, children and your relationships with them may all be affected as a result of the demands put on you.

If the person you care for shares your family home, sometimes you may feel you're being pulled in several directions at once. Planning ahead helps but changes in the amount of caring needed can upset the balance.

> *"We were happy for my 76-year-old father to come and live with us after my mother died. He had his own room and would join us for meals, but was always careful not to intrude. Then, two years ago, he had a massive stroke and I now find myself having to do much of the caring – dressing, bathing, toileting. I'm totally exhausted. My husband and I row all the time and I take it out on the children."*

Children can be quite resentful if a grandparent moves in and takes up time and space previously allotted to them. They may also find it embarrassing to invite friends back. As the carer you may be overwhelmed by your responsibilities and long for the days when you were just a normal family. There is no doubt that marriages do break up under this sort of strain and if things are getting difficult you need to seek help – respite care, counselling for yourself and maybe as a family, a rethink about your caring role.

◆ *Make time to be alone with your partner to talk about the situation at home but also just to enjoy each other's company.*

◆ *Organise breaks that you can enjoy as a family.*

◆ *Make sure your children have someone objective they can talk to if they're upset by the situation. If you have a social worker he or she may be able to help or you can approach the teacher in charge of pastoral care at your child's school.*

## Where to go for help

**FOR COUNSELLING**
British Association for Counselling
The Westminster Pastoral Foundation
The Samaritans
Relate (formerly the Marriage Guidance Council)
Youth Access
Childline
SPOD

**FOR RELAXATION/ MEDITATION**
British Holistic Medical Association
Relaxation for Living

Transcendental Meditation
National Retreat Association

**FOR FRIENDSHIP**
Conversation by Correspondence Through Friends by Post

**FOR INFORMATION ON CARERS' GROUPS**
Carers National Association

**FOR DEPRESSION**
Royal College of Psychiatrists leaflets

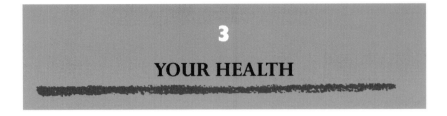

# 3

# YOUR HEALTH

Carers are tough. They have to be. They work long hours, take on more responsibility than most, often juggling several lives. Carers simply keep going. They may have no choice.

*"Actually I've grown physically and mentally stronger – I've had to."*

But you may be so concerned about the person you're caring for that you don't look after your own health. A recent Carers National Association survey showed that 65 per cent of carers said that their health was affected by caring, yet they dismissed potentially serious symptoms like high blood pressure, fainting and so on, insisting they were in quite good health.

Carers tend to suffer in silence and put up with exhaustion, bad backs, pulled muscles and various stress-related symptoms from headaches to indigestion. There's a feeling that as a carer, you can't give in to illness. Colds, flu, upset stomachs – minor ailments like these, which other people deal with by taking a few days off to recover – are dismissed by carers.

*"You've got to remember that if you have flu you can't go to bed – so you just add depression to your physical troubles."*

But struggling on gives your body little chance to recover and the exhaustion and tiredness make you more likely to succumb to the next bug going.

Chapter 2 talked about how easy it is to forget your own emotional needs. Your physical needs for a healthy diet, enjoyable exercise and a good night's sleep are as important. If you're physically fit you'll have more energy and be less likely to get draining illnesses, like colds.

It's not easy to be fully fit when you're a carer but it's possible, with just some small changes, to be fitter than you are now.

# Your physical needs

Caring for your physical needs means:

◆ *eating well-balanced meals to provide you with the energy you need to cope and the nutrients you need for general good health*

◆ *exercising to strengthen your muscles, joints, heart and lungs so that you can cope more easily with the physical effort involved in caring*

◆ *sleeping well, to let your mind and body recover from the demands of the day*

◆ *breaking bad habits, like smoking and drinking too much*

◆ *keeping an eye on yourself so that any minor ailments are dealt with in the early stages*

◆ *learning to recognise signs of stress and knowing how to deal with them.*

# Enjoying your food

Eating should be a pleasure. It's also a chance to sit down and relax. As a carer this may rarely happen – there may be no time and you may have someone else's likes and dislikes to consider.

**"I dreaded meal-times. My mother had become so finicky about her food – what she'd eat one day, she'd refuse the next. I was exasperated and worried at the same time. The answer for us was to let her be more involved in choosing the meals."**

**"Feeding my sister took such a long time that any appetite I'd had at the beginning just vanished. I regularly skipped meals and seemed to live off leftovers and the odd slice of bread."**

It's easy for your own food needs to drop into second place but without nourishing meals you won't have the energy to carry on.

### THE FOODS YOU NEED

Base your meals around fibre-rich, starchy foods like bread, potatoes, pasta and rice. Eat plenty of vegetables and fruit – fresh, frozen and canned. Each day, eat some meat, pulses, eggs or cheese, making lean and low-fat choices where possible. Foods like cakes, biscuits and crisps can be eaten as part of a healthy diet but should be eaten in small amounts and not as a replacement for other foods.

## FOODS TO GIVE YOU ENERGY

You probably work long days, either caring full-time or combining the caring with other roles, so you need the sort of energy that takes you steadily through and sustains you rather than the quick boost that you would get from sugary snacks. Fibre-rich, starchy foods like bread, potatoes, pasta and rice provide us with energy. They're filling and the wholemeal varieties also provide us with fibre.

## MAKING SMALL CHANGES TO THE WAY YOU EAT

There's no need to make dramatic changes to the way you eat to make your diet more healthy. Start by making small changes which you feel you can cope with and build on them.

- *Use semi-skimmed or skimmed milk, and try low-fat yoghurts and half-fat cheeses.*
- *Preferably choose a low-fat spread or margarine high in polyunsaturates. Whatever you spread on your bread, use sparingly.*
- *Trim the fat off meat, remove the skin from chicken and fish.*
- *Grill, poach or bake rather than fry. Avoid adding butter and margarine to vegetables and potatoes.*
- *Eat plenty of bread, potatoes, pasta and rice, particularly the wholemeal varieties.*
- *Eat fruit for desserts and snacks. Eat plenty of vegetables and salad. Avoid overcooking vegetables. Steam, pressure cook or cook in very little water, or stir fry in a little oil.*
- *Cut down on sugary foods and drinks, particularly those eaten between meals.*
- *Cut down on salt by not adding to the water when cooking vegetables or to your meal once it's on the plate. Herbs are a better way to add flavour.*
- *Don't forget to drink – 6 to 8 cups of fluid a day is recommended.*

# Getting started

**HERE ARE SOME SUGGESTIONS**

**Breakfast** Home-made muesli, with fresh fruit, like an apple or banana, and mixed with low-fat yoghurt or semi-skimmed milk. To make muesli: soak oats (porridge oats are fine) overnight in water or skimmed milk. Next morning add sliced banana, chopped apple or other fruit, 4 tbsp natural low-fat yoghurt and the juice of half an orange or 1 tbsp orange juice. Alternatively, add raisins, sultanas, or chopped, dried apricots.

**Main meal** A salad is easy to prepare. Use whatever comes to hand – lettuce, shredded red or white cabbage, grated carrot. Serve with plenty of bread or a jacket potato/boiled potatoes. Add tuna or sardines (in brine, drained) or low-fat cottage cheese.

Home-made soup can be tastier and cheaper than anything out of a tin or packet and doesn't take long to make. Gently stew chopped up leeks, potatoes and carrots in a saucepan. Add a pint of water or liquid left over from cooking vegetables. Cook for 20 minutes then liquidise or, if you haven't got a liquidiser, thicken the soup by adding a drained tin of cooked kidney or haricot beans or a handful of rice or pasta.

**ENJOY YOUR SNACKS**

The idea of eating three meals a day isn't carved in stone. If you skip meals it might be easier to have several snacks during the day. If you snack sensibly you'll still get all the nutrients you need.

> *"My cousin introduced me to the idea of six small meals a day when she came back from the States (they call it grazing). It suited me because my aunt still wanted her usual three meals a day and I was able to give her all my attention at meal-times instead of letting my own meal get cold or not bothering to eat."*

These little meals should contain as many nutrients as possible, so try not to snack on biscuits and cakes. Some snacks could be smaller versions of main meals but traditional snacks like toast on its own or with baked beans, egg, sardines or low-fat cheese; home-made soup and bread; toasted muffins, teacakes, sandwiches and filled pitta bread are all quick and easy. Have plenty of fruit around and keep carrot and celery sticks ready in the fridge to chew on.

Crispbreads, breadsticks and rice cakes are all good for snacking, as are breakfast cereals with skimmed or semi-skimmed milk and low-fat yoghurt and fromage frais.

## If you're overweight

*"I put on about a stone in the first six months of caring. I was stuck at home with my husband, never walked further than the end of the road and I was eating too much – but the food was my only comfort."*

It's easy to put on extra weight if you're a carer. You may eat lots of things just for comfort or because they're easier, you may eat more and yet be stuck in the home and get less exercise. If you're overweight it puts more strain on your body, particularly your back. You may also feel depressed about being fat.

If you're under stress you may not want to have to think about losing weight. However losing some weight can be quite a boost to your morale so if you do decide to go ahead here are some ways to make it easier:

◆ *Avoid crash diets. A sudden drop in calorie intake will make you weak when you need to be strong and you'll often put the weight back on quite quickly as soon as you return to normal eating.*

◆ *If you can involve the person you care for this could help you to keep going and make them feel involved too.*

*"My husband turned out to be the best of all at encouraging me to lose weight. I thought he wouldn't be interested but, in fact, it got him away from the TV as he spent ages working out suitable meals."*

◆ *Make exercise part of losing weight.*

### Where to go for help

Your GP or the practice nurse should be able to give you information on healthy eating. Supermarkets, large pharmacy chains, libraries and community centres often have free booklets on diet. Or you can contact the Health Education Authority.

# If you're drinking too much

It's easy to start drinking when you're a carer and your days are stressful. Relaxing with a glass of beer, sherry, wine or spirits at the end of the day is an easy habit to get into. A small amount of alcohol isn't necessarily bad – it's just a matter of being aware. One glass may lead to two or more, then you may begin to enjoy a drink or two at lunchtime. It happens quite easily and is very understandable.

Alcohol is not really the answer to unwinding at the end of the day. If you're depressed it can make you feel worse. You need to be alert as a carer – alcohol slows reactions.

**HOW MUCH IS SAFE?**
The recommended weekly alcohol intake for men is 21 units and 14 units for a woman. The difference is because women's bodies are usually smaller, contain more fat and less water – the alcohol stays longer in a woman's body and becomes more concentrated so the liver is more likely to be damaged.

How much is a unit? In a pub or bar it's one measure of alcohol. At home you'll be more generous so take this into account. There's the same amount of alcohol in a single whisky, a small glass of wine or sherry, a quarter of a pint of strong lager, beer or cider, or half a pint of ordinary beer, lager or cider. On average it takes an hour for the body to get rid of one unit.

**KNOW HOW MUCH YOU'RE DRINKING**
Keep a drink diary for a week. For example:

|  | *What* | *Where / when / who with* | *Units* | *Total* |
|---|---|---|---|---|
| Monday |  |  |  |  |
| Tuesday |  |  |  |  |
| Wednesday |  |  |  |  |
| Sunday |  |  |  |  |
| Total for the week |  |  |  |  |

## HOW TO CUT DOWN ON DRINKING

◆ *Use the drink diary to work out where and when you can cut down.*

◆ *Make one or two days a week alcohol-free. Replace the usual alcoholic drink with fruit juice or a non-alcohol cocktail.*

◆ *Drink slowly, use smaller measures.*

◆ *Dilute alcoholic drinks with mixers or water.*

◆ *Eat before you drink and don't drink alcohol if you're thirsty.*

◆ *If you feel you need help to control your drinking see your GP or phone Alcoholics Anonymous (0904 644026) or look under Alcohol in your phone book.*

# How to quit smoking

You may depend on smoking to help you cope but it does little to improve your general health. If you smoke in front of the person you care for, they'll be inhaling your fumes, which won't help their health either.

You may feel that smoking helps you cope with stress. You may imagine that it makes you feel relaxed but, in fact, nicotine is a stimulant. It increases the heart rate and alerts the brain. When the nicotine level falls you begin to feel edgy. Having another cigarette boosts the nicotine level and you feel better – the stress is actually caused by the withdrawal.

It's really hard to stop smoking – but you feel wonderful when you've conquered the habit. The first two to three weeks are usually awful – you may be bad tempered, you'll probably think of cigarettes all the time, even dream you're smoking – the temptation to just have one will be overwhelming. If you resist you'll be well on the way to being a committed non-smoker.

## WHAT ARE THE BENEFITS?

◆ *You'll breathe more easily.*

◆ *You'll have more energy.*

◆ *Food will taste better.*

◆ *You'l feel really proud of yourself.*

## THINK POSITIVE

- *Take it one day at a time.*
- *Many smokers quit several times before stopping for good. So don't be discouraged if you stop for a week or so and then start again. Each time you stop and then start again you'll be more determined to succeed next time.*
- *Remember, in the last 15 years, 10 million people have stopped smoking – and stayed stopped. That works out at over 1,000 every day. One of them could be you.*
- *Stop smoking because you want to – not because others tell you. You're more likely to stay stopped if the decision is yours.*

## ACTION PLAN

- *Choose a day to stop smoking.*
- *Tell friends and family your plan and get their support.*
- *Get rid of all traces of smoking: ashtrays, matches, lighters, empty packets, etc.*
- *Plan a reward by putting the money saved each day to one side.*
- *Break the links. If you always have a cigarette with your first cup of coffee, don't have coffee for a while, avoid pubs and bars and other smoke-filled places.*
- *You may want something to put in your mouth – have a supply of chewing gum or boiled sweets in the house.*
- *Find something else to do with your hands – fiddle with a pencil or some beads.*
- *Don't think about tomorrow – just congratulate yourself at the end of each day.*

You could try using nicotine chewing gum or nicotine patches which you can get from pharmacists.

> **"The day I decided to stop smoking I treated myself to a massage. I came out feeling so relaxed that I didn't even want a cigarette. The cravings came the next day but by then I'd made that important start and it was just a little easier to keep it up."**

**FOR MORE INFORMATION**

Your GP or practice nurse will also be able to help. ASH (Action on Smoking and Health) can put you in touch with a local self-help group and offer advice.

## Looking after yourself

Make time for your physical health despite other demands.

- ◆ *See your GP if you have symptoms such as fainting, a persistent cough, depression, or exhaustion.*
- ◆ *Note any skin changes such as moles which enlarge, darken or bleed.*
- ◆ *If you're over 75 your GP should offer you a full medical check-up each year. Make sure you attend so that any changes in your health can be dealt with in the early stages. Below 75, see your GP for a check up to measure blood pressure, weight, etc., every three years.*
- ◆ *If you're a woman make sure you have regular cervical cancer screenings. All women aged 20 to 64 should have a smear test every five years. Contact your GP or FPA clinic to make sure you're on the register.*
- ◆ *If you're a woman aged between 50 and 65 you should make use of the mammograms offered on the NHS. Whatever your age examine your breasts once a month and note any changes such as unusual lumps. Even if you simply suspect a change, see your GP.*

## Getting the best from your GP

- ◆ *Make sure you let your GP know you're a carer.*
- ◆ *Go prepared. Make a list of the things you want to ask or say, include even things that seem unimportant. The more the GP knows about you, the easier it is for him or her to help.*
- ◆ *If you're given a prescription and suffer side effects let your GP know as soon as possible. There may be other drugs to try.*
- ◆ *Don't feel you're wasting your GP's time.*
- ◆ *If you believe you're not being taken seriously, keep repeating firmly what you feel is wrong.*

◆ *Try and make notes of what the GP says while you're in the surgery. You can refer to them later.*

◆ *If you feel your GP isn't really listening or you're unhappy with your treatment you can change to another doctor (see Chapter 4 on how to do this).*

## Caring for your back

For many carers a healthy, pain-free back is a thing of the past. If you regularly have to lift someone or help them dress, wash or go to the toilet, you're asking a lot of your back. If you're handling the person wrongly or they're too heavy for you, your back will let you know.

You can also create your own back problems through poor posture and sheer fatigue. REMEMBER – IF YOUR BACK HURTS DON'T IGNORE IT – SEEK HELP.

◆ *See your GP. You may be prescribed a short course of painkillers or drugs to lessen inflammation. You could be offered physiotherapy sessions if the pain continues (they're usually available on the NHS although there may be a long waiting list).*

◆ *Once your GP has assured you that your back pain is not due to any other illness or disease you may wish to seek complementary treatment, for example, osteopathy, chiropractic and acupuncture can all relieve and, in some cases, cure back pain.*

◆ *Try and rest your back as much as possible.*

If you know that your back problem is due to lifting the person you care for:

◆ *Ask your GP to refer you to the community physiotherapist or district nurse to visit and assess your needs.*

◆ *They may suggest quite simple aids to lifting and handling such as slings, transfer boards or a turntable, or you may need larger items such as a hoist or lift.*
   *Ask the social services department for advice on how these can be supplied and paid for (see Chapter 4).*

◆ *These trained people can also show you how to handle the person you care for correctly by allowing him or her to help himself as much as possible.*

Experts will tell you never to lift unless it's absolutely essential (e.g. in an emergency) and never to lift anyone on your own who weighs more than 5 stone. But if you're caring alone, with no extra help, you have little choice at times. That's why it's important to get the co-operation of the person you're caring for. It may take longer to do some things as a result but your back will benefit.

## BEFORE YOU LIFT

◆ *Tell the person what you're going to do so that they are able to help as much as possible.*

◆ *Get in the right position: feet apart, one foot pointing in the direction of the move, the other close to the person being moved; relaxed knees; head held up and in line with back.*

◆ *Only move a little way at a time.*

◆ *Avoid twisting your back by keeping the person in front of you.*

◆ *Tighten your stomach muscles before you move or lift to strengthen your back.*

## EXERCISES FOR YOUR BACK

The secret of a strong back lies in the muscles that surround it. The muscles that lie alongside the spine are the ones most likely to be strained and they can be helped if you have strong stomach muscles. Gentle pull-up exercises strengthen these but only go as far as feels comfortable. Leg raises while lying on your stomach on the floor also help.

### FOR MORE INFORMATION
The National Back Pain Association has produced a carer's guide on moving and handling patients. The Osteopathic Information Service, British Chiropractors' Association and British Acupuncture Association can recommend a qualified therapist in your area. See Chapter 6 for more information on the practicalities of lifting and ways to make life easier.

◆ Lie on your stomach on the floor

◆ Slowly lift your left leg away from the floor, as far as is comfortable

◆ Slowly relax down, and repeat with the other leg

◆ Lie on your back with your knees bent, and feet flat on the floor

◆ Put your hands on top of your thighs

◆ Lifting your head and shoulders off the floor, slide your fingers along your thighs a little

◆ Then uncurl slowly back to the lying position

# Exercise

### WHY YOU NEED EXERCISE

*"Some days I just didn't feel in the mood, especially if I'd had a bad night. But, however tired I was, once I got to the leisure centre I found that I enjoyed the class, could do the exercises and felt really good. It was a different sort of weariness I suppose."*

If you spend your days running around caring for someone then you're probably doing more exercise than the average person sitting behind a desk in an office. But there's a difference between the physical demands of your role as a carer and spending perhaps a couple of hours a week doing an exercise that you enjoy and that you have chosen.

Exercise really can be fun and that may be something that's missing from your life. It may take an effort to get started and to keep going, but once you establish a routine, exercise can become an enjoyable part of your life.

## WHAT CAN EXERCISE DO FOR YOU?

Three things help you to be physically fit: suppleness, strength and stamina. Suppleness in your joints and strong muscles will help you to do everyday tasks easily and with less risk of injury. If you build up your stamina by exercising your heart and lungs through aerobic exercise, like brisk walking, jogging, swimming, as well as having a healthier cardio-vascular system, your muscles will receive a better supply of blood and work more efficiently.

REMEMBER: IF YOU EXERCISE FOR TWENTY MINUTES A DAY, THREE TIMES A WEEK, YOU'LL FEEL THE BENEFIT AFTER JUST TWELVE WEEKS.

Exercise can also make you feel happier, more relaxed. It can certainly help to relieve stress. There's evidence to show that this is caused by the release of endorphins, substances in the brain which contribute to a feeling of well-being.

*"It was gradual but I began to notice that after a swim I'd feel on top of the world. I'd go home and be cheerful for the rest of the day."*

# Dealing with stress

Stress isn't all bad – we need some in order to keep going – and it can make us feel quite exhilarated. But the sort of stress you can experience as a carer is the kind that can make you feel worried, helpless and insecure.

The body responds to any stressful situation by getting ready to face danger. The heart beats faster, breathing speeds up, chemicals flow into the system to enable the muscles to be used. This response is known as the 'fight or flight' reaction and although it's ideal in a situation where some physical action is needed, if the cause is simply pressure of living, then there's no chance to release this energy. The result is an almost permanent feeling of tension.

The relaxation techniques in Chapter 2 are a good way to manage stress but exercise can also help because it gives you a chance to channel all that pent-up energy into something physical. The problems still need solving but you may feel, once you're in a regular exercise routine, that you can approach them more calmly and methodically.

## CHOOSE SOMETHING THAT'S RIGHT FOR YOU

If there's a leisure centre nearby, you'll have a chance to try a variety of activities – swimming, aerobic classes, Step, body building, keep fit and stretching classes. You may want to do a couple of different classes.

*"Finding time to exercise wasn't easy. When my aunt was at the day centre, I shopped or did housework. I had to change my priorities but it was worth it because the extra energy I had from exercise meant I did the chores that much faster and somehow they seemed less important too."*

## SOME SUGGESTIONS

**Walking** is safe, effective and doesn't need a lot of organisation or special equipment (so it's cheap).

◆ *To benefit you need to do more than just stroll to the shops. But it can be easier to establish a routine if you walk close to home, say, round the block.*

◆ *Start slowly, walking for 20 to 30 minutes, three to four times a week at a comfortable pace. Gradually increase your speed until you're walking for the same length of time but going further without becoming out of breath.*

◆ *Wear comfortable shoes.*

**Exercise classes** Like aquafit these give you a chance to exercise safely in the company of other people. Many people say that the social side of exercising gives them as much as the physical benefits.

**Swimming** is good because the support of water makes injury unlikely. It can help if you have a bad back or joint problem. Again, start slowly, swimming for 10 to 15 minutes with breaks in between lengths. Try to use a variety of strokes so that all the muscles are being exercised. It may be  harder to find the time to swim but once a week is ideal if you combine it with another form of exercise. Many pools have aquafit classes where you can do gentle stretching in the safety of the water – and maybe make new friends.

**Cycling** is a simple way to exercise. Make sure you include some hills when you cycle as you need to put some effort in – otherwise your ride will be no more than the equivalent of a gentle stroll. If you want company then contact your local cyclists' touring club.

If it's very difficult to get away from your caring responsibilities you could think of buying an exercise bike or a rowing machine. It needs more dedication to keep using these as they soon lose their appeal – on the other hand, this makes it easier to buy a second-hand model!

A few words of caution:

♦ *If you haven't done any exercise for a while, are over 35 or have had any health problems in the past (or present), check with your GP before starting any exercise programme.*

♦ *Always start slowly. It's better to walk round the block for 10 minutes than go all out for 20 and pull a muscle, or return so exhausted that you can't do any more exercise that week.*

♦ *If you get any pain or discomfort while exercising – stop.*

♦ *Always do some warm-up exercises beforehand if you're going to exercise vigorously. For example, simple bending and stretching.*

♦ *If you're walking, swimming or cycling you can warm up by starting slowly.*

♦ *When you've finished the session, do some gentle stretching again to help cool down.*

**FOR MORE INFORMATION**
Sports Council, the Health Education Authority.

# Sleeping as well as you can

Sleep is a wonderful gift. Unfortunately, if you're worried, stressed, over-tired or in pain, a good night's sleep will be hard to achieve. Some carers have their sleep interrupted night after night by the person they care for and there is advice on what to do in Chapter 6. But what if it's you who can't sleep…?

*"I fall into bed, exhausted, at about 10pm, go to sleep and wake up a couple of hours later. I then spend the rest of the night tossing and turning. By morning I'm a wreck."*

*"I lay there every night just listening to her breathing. If I did drop off, I'd be awake in an instant if she so much as moved or sighed. I was so afraid."*

**WHAT YOU CAN DO**

◆ *Make bedtime as relaxing as possible: have a warm bath, a hot drink, but avoid stimulants in tea, coffee, alcohol, cigarettes, cola drinks. Do relaxation or meditation exercises (see Chapter 2). These can all help you to unwind after a heavy day.*

◆ *If you wake in the night, don't lie there tossing and turning. Put on the light, read, listen to the radio, make yourself a hot drink.*

*"If I do something while I'm awake I feel better. At least it's not time wasted. I do the ironing or watch a video. After a couple of hours out of bed, I make myself a hot water bottle and a milk drink and it's easier for me to go to sleep again."*

◆ *Exercise during the day (but not just before bedtime) can help you to sleep better.*

◆ *It often helps not to have your main meal in the evening.*

◆ *Keep to a routine. Even if you sleep badly, get up at the usual time in the morning rather than trying to make up for lost sleep.*

◆ *Make your bedroom as comfortable and welcoming as you can so that you feel warm and cosy in bed.*

◆ *Many carers would prefer not to take drugs to help them sleep because the person they care for may need them in the night, or perhaps they fear becoming addicted. But sometimes a mild sedative for a short time can help break the pattern.*

As a carer you have a right to receive support for a valuable job. Doctors, social workers and other paid professionals are part of a network that you can call on. But some carers have mixed feelings about accepting this help or even asking for it. It's also easy to feel discouraged if you live in an area which is poorly served and where even simple requests, such as a few hours' break from caring, are turned down. You may recognise some of the following remarks:

> *"When I married my husband, I promised to look after him in sickness and in health. Now he needs me it would feel wrong to ask for anyone else to help."*

> *"There's no point asking when the answer is bound to be no."*

> *"Of course I get tired but I'm the best person to look after Dad. I know he'd be unhappy if anyone else came in."*

> *"When I finally got up the courage to go to social services I was told we didn't qualify. I'm not going to them again."*

> *"I'm not a full-time carer so I probably don't qualify for any sort of help."*

> *"My life is too busy as it is. I just haven't got time to fill out forms, go for interviews. It's easier to just keep going on my own."*

> *"I don't know who does what or even where to go."*

> *"I'm not accepting charity."*

> *"I don't want strangers in my home knowing my business."*

There are probably dozens of other reasons, but since support for carers is now one of the key objectives of the Community Care Act, there is awareness of carers' needs and there are professionals who can offer information, advice and help in a sensitive way.

What's available varies from area to area and you may not get exactly what you ask for but as one carer put it: "Take help when it's offered – you might not get asked again."

One of the surest ways to improve or even initiate a service is to make sure the people who make the decisions know there's a demand for it. It may not be easy for you because often you have to call on your own energies to organise some of the support you need and you probably already have enough to do. In an ideal world, things would certainly be the other way round, but by making good use of the professionals that are there you can ease the way to getting the help needed.

Here are some ideas to get you started and keep you going:

◆ *Be informed. Gather as much information as possible about what's available.*

◆ *If there's something you don't understand ask to have it explained. This includes form-filling – there are people who will help – if you ask them.*

◆ *Be persistent. If the answer is no, don't give up. Keep repeating what you want again and again.*

◆ *Know what your priorities are.*

◆ *Be flexible. If one particular service isn't available, there may be an alternative.*

◆ *Don't be embarrassed about asking for help to do your job as a carer. It's not a sign of weakness but of strength, showing that you understand the situation and your needs within it.*

◆ *Be part of the team. Your role as carer and the knowledge you have is a vital part of decision-making – as a carer you often know best what is right.*

◆ *Plan ahead. Think about the support you may need in the future and put in a request in good time*

◆ *If possible join forces with other carers. You'll be able to give each other support and encouragement.*

# Knowing what you want

If you know what you and the person you care for need, your requests can be clearly and directly stated. Ideally, discuss things with the person you care for and the rest of the family if it's appropriate. Or you could talk to friends, relatives or other carers.

Many people find it useful to keep a 'care diary'. You may be so busy caring and coping that you have no time to even start to think what help you might need. Keeping a diary for a week can clarify exactly what you do for the person you care for and help pinpoint the areas in which you need help. You may be able to fill out your diary together with the person you care for. Some counties have introduced a Carer's Assessment Module which carers fill out and then discuss with their social worker or district nurse.

## CARE DIARY

| Time | Job | How long taken |
|------|-----|----------------|
|      |     |                |
|      |     |                |
|      |     |                |
|      |     |                |
|      |     |                |
|      |     |                |
|      |     |                |

You could have a separate diary which lists the other things you do each day, for example, looking after the family, commitments such as a job or voluntary work.

Writing everything down will help you see how you spend your time. You can highlight ways of being better organised, creating more time for yourself.

*"I always used to bath my mother at night. By the time I'd finished I was drained. Filling out a care diary made me see that I could bathe her in the morning, when I had more energy. Mum agreed and it's made a great difference because I feel the evenings are much more my own."*

# People who can offer support

**Your family doctor (GP)** GPs take care of your health and the health of the person you care for. They refer you to other professionals for help and advice and give you information about what's available. A good GP, who understands and sympathises with the strains and stresses of caring, can be a valuable asset.

> *"My GP's wonderful. She makes sure I have an appointment at the end of surgery so there's time to talk. If she can't help directly she always seems to know someone who can."*

Often a GP won't have that time, while others can be very unconcerned (for advice on how to change your GP see later in this chapter). At the very least, a GP should be able to direct you to people who can offer the information, advice and support you need.

## MAKING THE MOST OF YOUR GP

It's important to let your GP know that you've become a carer, if possible in the early stages. Unless you or the person you care for have been seeing the GP regularly, he or she is unlikely to know about your changed circumstances.

You may have the same GP as the person you care for or you may prefer to have separate GPs. A shared GP may have a better understanding of the situation but some people find it easier to talk to a GP who doesn't actually know the person they care for – it makes it easier to be honest about negative feelings for instance.

Here are some more ways (in addition to those in Chapter 3) in which you can get the best out of your GP and what she or he has to offer.

◆ *Make a long enough appointment. If you want to discuss the person you care for or any particular problems, tell the receptionist who will be able to arrange a good time – usually at the end of surgery.*

◆ *If the person you care for is with the same GP and you wish to discuss something about him or her, then make sure the receptionist knows so that both sets of records are put out for the GP to refer to.*

◆ *If the person you care for is registered with a different GP but you want to take him or her to your own GP for a consultation, again let the receptionist know.*

- *Try and build up a good relationship with your GP — you'll get better care that way.*
- *If you want the GP to visit the person you care for at home, make it clear if it's not an emergency and give times when you, the carer, will be there.*
- *Allow time for prescriptions to be prepared. Keep an eye on what the person you care for (or you) needs and ask for a new prescription in good time.*

## PEOPLE YOUR GP MIGHT SUGGEST YOU SEE

All the people your GP can refer you to have special skills they can offer. Use your diary to help you see how best they can help you and the person you care for.

**Practice nurse:** is a qualified nurse based in the surgery, working alongside the GP. She offers general nursing services – dressings, injections, health screening and advice on general health. She may visit you at home to carry out an assessment on behalf of the GP.

**District nurse:** a qualified nurse with extra training in nursing people at home. She can visit the person you care for to change dressings and may help with bathing and toileting. She should be able to advise you on practical problems such as lifting and handling incontinence. She may also offer advice on aids and equipment, like hoists, commodes, special beds and mattresses. There may be an auxiliary nurse available to help with bathing. You don't have to be referred by your GP, you can contact her yourself through the receptionist at the surgery.

**Night nurse:** will provide nursing care for a very ill person or for someone with long-term needs. She can also offer you, the carer, respite if you're having to care day and night.

**Health visitor:** specialises in child health but increasingly trained to offer support and advice to other groups such as the elderly, disabled or people discharged from hospital.

**Counsellor:** a counsellor is not medically qualified (although many doctors take on a counselling role with patients). He or she can offer advice and support, usually over a particular problem, but also with more general feelings and attitudes. You will be encouraged to talk about your feelings, problems. These will then be discussed and explored. Some GPs now have qualified counsellors attached to their practice.

**Psychotherapist:** will use psychological methods to treat a patient. It can include hypnotherapy, behaviour therapy and group therapy.

Psychotherapists may be qualified psychiatrists or have some specialised training.

**Psychoanalyst:** many are medically qualified doctors but others may be fully trained social workers or psychiatric nurses. They offer treatment of mental or nervous disorders devised by Sigmund Freud.

**Psychiatrist:** is a medically qualified doctor who can treat patients with minor and major forms of mental illness.

**Speech therapist:** can help the person you care for with speech, swallowing and feeding problems.

**Dietician:** can be especially useful if the person you care for is difficult to feed or is off their food. Or can advise you about your own diet.

**Consultant/specialist:** only your GP can refer you to a specialist. He or she will usually work within a hospital and can be seen on the NHS or privately – either at the hospital or at consulting rooms. Consultants are fully qualified doctors who have chosen to specialise in a particular field, e.g. neurology, orthopaedics, geriatrics. If your GP seems reluctant to refer you, be persistent. If you're dissatisfied with the specialist's views you may ask your GP for a further referral for a second opinion.

**Chiropodist:** offers foot care to people of 65 and over. In some areas this is extended to 60 to 64-year-olds.

**Community psychiatric nurse:** can visit you at home to help with treating people with mental health problems. As well as practical advice and support for you and your family he/she may be able to suggest organisations that can help.

**Occupational therapist (OT):** (see also social services) is trained to be able to assess the daily needs of elderly or disabled people in order to suggest practical ways of coping with things like dressing and bathing. Should be able to advise on equipment to make life easier, from small items like electric tin openers and special cutlery to lifts, hoists, ramps and bath seats.

**Physiotherapist (physio):** is trained to offer therapeutic massage and gentle exercise to maintain mobility and ease pain. Can also work with occupational therapist (OT) to advise on aids and equipment. Will advise carers on lifting and aids to make this easier and safer.

**Continence advisor:** offers specialist help and advice on incontinence (for more details see Chapter 6).

**Complementary therapist:** more and more surgeries have links with complementary therapies like osteopathy, chiropractic, acupuncture, hypnotherapy and reflexology. Treatment is rarely free but fees may be adjusted to take account of your financial situation.

### A GP MAY ALSO HELP TO ORGANISE THE FOLLOWING

**Hospice care:** specialist nursing care either at home or in a residential home for the terminally ill. You can find out more yourself from the Hospice Information Service, Cancer Relief (Macmillan Fund), Marie Curie Cancer Care or CancerLink.

**Short hospital stays:** for the person you care for – to give you a break.

**Day hospital treatment:** if the person you care for needs regular treatment. There may be transport by ambulance. Some hospitals offer recreational activities.

### THE HEALTH HELPLINE – 0800 665544

This freephone information line has information on all aspects of health from NHS services to hospital waiting lists; from common diseases to ways to keep healthy. Wherever you live you'll be automatically connected to the office for your particular area. The information and contact names, addresses and phone numbers will be local ones.

### MAKING A COMPLAINT

In England and Wales, National Health Service (NHS) users are represented by Community Health Councils (CHCs). In Scotland: Local Health Councils; in Northern Ireland: District Committees. These are independent bodies and there's one for each area.

The CHCs are there if you want to make a complaint about treatment you received or any other experience with the health service. All matters are dealt with confidentially.

You can find your local CHC in the phone book under Community; local Citizen's Advice Bureau; library; or from the local council information officer.

## Using the social services

Social services help comes via your local authority – your district, borough or county council (Health Board in Scotland; HPSS in Northern Ireland) . The local authority provides: social workers, home helps, occupational therapists, physiotherapists, key workers and case/care managers. They may also provide day centres, residential homes, meals on wheels and transport.

The Community Care Act means that local authorities have powers to arrange services to help older and disabled people remain in their own homes. As a carer your knowledge of the situation should be valued and your needs taken into account.

## HOW TO FIND OUT WHAT'S AVAILABLE

All local authorities are supposed to publish information about the sort of care services available in their area. These leaflets should be displayed in places like GPs' surgeries and the local library. They should tell you what services are available, how decisions are made on who gets help, how much help you should be able to get and what to do if you feel you're not getting what you need.

If you can't find the leaflets, phone your local social services department (look in the phone book under the name of your county council. Or ring the Town Hall).

## THE PEOPLE YOU MAY DEAL WITH

**Care manager** In some areas these people are employed within social services to specialise in care in the community. If there's one in your area it can make things easier because he or she will be fully aware of everything on offer and be involved in co-ordinating services. May also be referred to as a case manager or key worker. You can approach the care manager directly by phoning social services.

**Social worker** If there is no care manager then your main contact with social services will be via a social worker. A social worker must tell you what's available locally from social services and he/she should also be able to put you in touch with local voluntary organisations and carers' groups.

To contact a social worker you may have to make the first move. Either phone your local social services department and ask to speak to a social worker, or ask at your GP surgery or health centre as there may be a social worker attached there.

Increasingly social workers specialise in areas such as the elderly, disabled or children, so ask if you can be assigned to someone with specialist knowledge.

If the person you care for is in hospital contact the hospital social worker. He or she may be able to start the ball rolling so that the services you need are in place when your dependant comes home.

## WHAT THEY CAN DO FOR YOU

A social worker can organise a variety of supportive services: meals-on-wheels, home help, free laundry service, occupational therapy, physiotherapy, aids and equipment, advice on adapting or altering the home, respite care (whether for a few hours a week or some days away), an orange badge for parking, transport. He or she should also give advice on the various allowances and grants you and the person you care for are entitled to (see Chapter 5).

Lack of funds may mean that many services you would like simply can't be provided or you may have to wait a long time. For instance the need for care attendants to help with bathing and dressing far exceeds the supply. A sympathetic social worker will do all he or she can to get round this but suggesting alternatives may help.

Try to make your needs clear so that you're not forced to accept a service that's unnecessary or unsuitable.

## WHAT YOU CAN DO

◆ *Ask and keep asking. Don't take no for an answer.*
◆ *Ask your social worker if there are any voluntary groups that can help you.*
◆ *Call on family and friends for help with shopping, cooking and housework.*
◆ *Write to your local council, parish councillor or MP to complain about the lack of services.*
◆ *Get together with members of your local carers' support group to put pressure on the local authority to provide what is needed.*

## RESPITE CARE

There are two types of respite care available through social services:

**Category 1** usually involves someone coming to the home to look after the person you care for while you have a break. This could be just a few hours a week or it might allow you to have a week away.

**Category 2** means offering help away from home, say, at a day centre, where there will be various activities like singing or craftwork and social contact for the person you care for. Respite care in nursing homes and day hospitals offering treatment also come into this category.

Other types of respite care can be arranged by your social worker, GP, health visitor, district nurse or voluntary groups:

**Adult Placement Schemes** These allow the person you care for to stay with a local family either every day, once in a while or for longer periods.

**Hospital care** Short- and long-term beds may be available but are in very short supply.

## ASSESSMENTS – WHAT'S INVOLVED

Social services have to assess anyone they feel needs community care services in order to draw up a package of what's needed. Usually the social worker arranges the assessment. If the need is quite simple, for instance, a grab rail by the bath, then just one person – maybe the social worker or occupational therapist – will be involved in the assessment. If the needs are more complex, a nurse or physiotherapist may also be involved (this is then called a 'multi-disciplinary assessment').

Each local authority carries out assessments differently. Information on how they do this should be available in writing from social services, the Citizen's Advice Bureau, or even in hospital.

The assessment may take place in your home or at the social services office. Two things are considered: care needs and assessment of finances and they should be looked at separately.

People doing assessments often try to make you and the person you care for adapt to what is available, rather than considering what's actually right for you, so you'll need to be quite adamant about what you feel is best.

There should be a written record of the assessment including areas of disagreement and services that you feel are needed but which the local authority can't provide. Once a decision has been made you should receive a care plan from the authority. It will show what they will provide and what will be offered by others (e.g. by a voluntary organisation). If things change you can also ask for a review.

If at all possible, the person you care for will be asked for their thoughts. As a carer your contribution is essential. If you can talk to the person you care for before the assessment takes place this will help you both to be clear about what is needed. Refer to your care diary to highlight priorities.

## WHO PAYS?

The person you care for will be means-tested. As a carer you have no responsibility to pay for services for the person you care for, although in some circumstances spouses may be asked to pay.

## HOW TO COMPLAIN

If you disagree with an assessment; if you find your social worker more of a hindrance than a help; if you don't see eye to eye with your GP – you don't have to sit there and take it – you can act.

# Changing your GP

If you find that your GP isn't providing the sort of care you expect, you have a choice of actions:

1. It may be possible to transfer to another GP in the same practice. This will allow you to continue your relationship with the practice for other members of the family. Remember that your GP may be the duty doctor when you call. If there has been a relationship problem this may cause difficulty.
2. You could ask the practice manager if the practice has an informal complaints procedure. many GPs prefer to handle complaints within the practice. Your difficulty might easily be resolved.
3. You have the right to change doctor. You may already know about another doctor in the area. You could telephone or visit the practice to see if they'll take you on. If you or your relative are housebound it is important to let the practice know. It may be best to ask to speak to the doctor concerned so that you are aware of what he or she is able to offer.
4. You can contact the FHSA – they hold a list of practitioners: doctors, dentists, pharmacists and opticians. The FHSA will then find you a doctor in your area who'll accept you.

If you wish to complain about the service provided, it's often best to start informally as outlined above. If you feel that the matter is serious, you should write to the FHSA (Primary Care Committee in Scotland, Central Services Agency in Northern Ireland) within 13 weeks of the problem occurring. A senior officer will then reply, explaining what's involved. You can also contact your local Community Health Council (CHC) (Local Health Council in Scotland, District Committee in Northern Ireland). The CHC can't investigate your complaint but can provide information and advice on the next steps.

### QUERYING AN ASSESSMENT

Ask for a written statement of the assessment and for reasons why the help you need has not been included. Contact your local social services department. There will be a specific person there who deals with complaints and who will explain the procedure. He or she should also be able to put you in touch with someone who can help you put your concerns across.

# Changing your social worker

It's often hard to be objective when a social worker refuses you a service you need. In many cases it may be simply because of local authority cutbacks rather than the social worker's belief that you don't qualify for the extra support.

However, if there is real conflict and you feel the social worker is working against you rather than for you, then you can ask to be transferred to a colleague. It might also help you to see the supervisor in the social work department. It will give you a chance to explain how you feel and maybe find a solution.

# Learning to be noticed

The support services are surrounded by people clamouring for their attention. As a carer you need to be determined, persistent and efficient – not easy when you're worn out. In the words of other carers you must, "speak up, speak out and keep doing it", "ask and keep asking," "recognise your power, remember they need you more than you need them."

Treating your contacts with the support services in a business-like manner can be very helpful. Here are some suggestions from carers:

◆ *When someone from social services comes to see you, make sure you write down their name, their department, exactly what their job is, where they work from and how they can be contacted.*

◆ *Keep a file or box of everything to do with the person you care for and the support services. You could have different sections: for health, money, daily help/support. You can file everything that happens, who you talked to, what they said and so on. When you're under strain and anxious it's easy to forget things, so keeping a file will help.*

## USING THE PHONE EFFICIENTLY

Many things are organised or decided over the telephone these days, so it's useful to be able to use the phone to your advantage. Here are some guidelines:

◆ *Write a list of the things you want to talk about.*
◆ *Try and have a named person to ask for.*
◆ *If you don't know the person's name, switchboard operators can usually be helpful.*

◆ *If the person you want to speak to isn't there, leave a message: including your name, your telephone number and some information that gives an idea of why you're phoning. You could say something like. "Can you tell her it's Susan Smith, I care for / look after John Jones. Could she please phone me as soon as possible regarding… . My phone number is … and I'm here all day / most mornings."*

◆ *If your call isn't returned, phone again. If there's still no response ask to speak to a colleague. If this is still unsatisfactory, ask to speak to the supervisor or write a letter stating that you have phoned on several occasions and received no reply and repeating the reason for your call. Send this letter to the person you wish to contact, with a copy to the head of department and keep a copy for yourself.*

◆ *If you're given any information over the phone do write it down so that you can refer to it later.*

◆ *Keep pen and paper by the phone so that you can log the date and time of phone calls.*

◆ *Don't be embarrassed about asking people to repeat details or information.*

◆ *If anything is suggested or agreed over the phone ask for it to be confirmed in writing. Write your own letter, summarising the conversation. Date all correspondence, even a scribbled note, and keep a copy.*

# Other people who can help

Apart from the health professionals, voluntary groups can help you in all sorts of ways. Increasingly, social services and the health services are using them. Among them will be Age Concern, Help the Aged, Crossroads, WRVS, the British Red Cross (see Chapter 10). Then there are the organisations for specific diseases and illnesses such as Alzheimer's Disease Society, The Stroke Association, CancerLink. Most have local groups and all can offer advice and support. WRVS, for example, have their meals-on-wheels service; the Red Cross has equipment like wheelchairs and commodes that can be hired; Help the Aged has a free telephone advice line: 0800 289 404. The Disabled Living Foundation can offer advice on choosing aids and equipment and some areas may have a Disabled Living

Centre where you can go and look at a permanent exhibition of equipment. There will be an occupational therapist available to answer questions. RADAR (Royal Association for Disability and Rehabilitation) has useful information on access, mobility and what social services should be providing.

The DSS publishes a booklet on equipment and services for people with disabilities. You can get a copy from your local benefits office or write to Health Publications Unit, No 2 Site, Heywood Stores, Manchester Road, Heywood, Lancashire OL10 2PZ.

# Carers' groups

The greatest amount of support and advice can come from other carers – people like yourself. By talking to someone who's faced a similar situation you may find answers to some of your difficulties. Other carers can also give you the extra courage you need to fight for something you know is needed.

There may be several carers' support groups in the area: a general group, one for stroke victims or for carers of people with specific illnesses or from a particular section of the community.

## FINDING A GROUP
- *Contact the Carers National Association head office for information on groups in your area (see Chapter 10).*
- *Ask your GP, practice or district nurse or social worker if they know of any carers' groups.*
- *If the person you care for has an illness or disability contact the national organisation as they may have a local carers' group.*
- *Ask at the Citizen's Advice Bureau (CAB) or local library.*

*"I wasn't keen on going to the local carers' group. I thought it would be really depressing – just sitting around talking about our problems. Well, there is some of that but there are other things. We laugh together, sometimes we cry and it's somewhere where I can go and let off steam. I go home refreshed."*

**"I went to one carers' meeting but it was so difficult to organise I gave up. But the group organiser came round to see how I was. She understands I can rarely get out but has kept in touch and I don't feel so cut off."**

Some groups are very organised – they produce their own literature, run a formal advice service, have phone information lines. Others campaign for improvements in services. Some are run by carers, others by social services. All are there for carers to use for mutual support.

This may not suit everyone, although it's worth visiting your local group a few times before you make a final decision. The first visit can be quite nerve-wracking – although everyone will make you feel welcome. If this is holding you back you could contact the group organiser and see if there is someone nearby with whom you can go.

But some people need other outlets.

**"When I leave the house I need to forget I'm a carer. I'd lost touch with the people I knew when I was at work. The practice nurse suggested I went to an aerobics class – mainly to improve my fitness. I made friends there and now each week we do the class and have a snack lunch at the leisure centre afterwards."**

**IF THERE IS NO CARERS' GROUP**

You may want to start up a group if there's nothing for carers in your area. The Carers National Association (see Chapter 10) has an information pack giving details on how to set up a self-help or support group. There's also a pack on how to set up a local branch.

If you're going it on your own you could start by talking to your GP, social worker, district nurse or health visitor. You may be able to put a notice up in the surgery inviting interested people to the first meeting or you could write to your local paper or parish magazine.

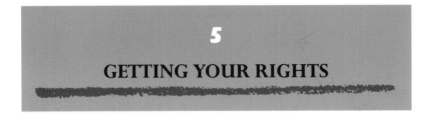

# 5
# GETTING YOUR RIGHTS

If you care for someone, both you and the person you care for may be entitled to a number of benefits from the Department of Social Security and the local authority. There are regular weekly payments, one-off grants, benefits that are paid for a limited period. Some will be paid to the person you care for, others are paid to you, the carer.

Many people don't apply for benefits. Sometimes it's because they feel it's like asking for charity, more often it's because claiming is so complex. Although attempts have been made to simplify matters, forms do remain long, means-tested benefits (which ask for details of your income and savings) need a lot of effort to fill out and often you may not want to be bothered. The added aggravation is that it often takes months for applications to be processed and that can be very disheartening. However, the benefits are there and even if you're unsure about whether you qualify or not, it's always worth applying.

The Benefits Agency (DSS) and the local authority will both accept applications made by carers on behalf of the person cared for. They'll also send a visiting officer to your home if it's very difficult for you to get to your local office.

Allowances are changing all the time – some are rolled together, others may act as a passport to others, the amounts paid out change annually. In this chapter there's a guide to the allowances that are relevant for you. There are several general guides available that explain benefits and allowances in detail such as the *Disability Rights Handbook* and Age Concern's *Your Rights*. The DSS also produce a general guide *Which Benefit?* as well as leaflets on individual benefits and allowances. You can get these from post offices, libraries, Citizen's Advice Bureaux and social security offices.

It also helps to have someone to talk to who can explain things. The DSS freephone 0800 666 555 for mainland Britain (0800 616 757 for Northern Ireland) gives general advice.

The Benefits Enquiry Line (BEL) for disabled people and carers, (weekdays 8.30am–6.30pm: Saturdays 9am–1pm) freephone 0800 882 200 for mainland Britain (0800 220 674 for Northern Ireland) will give advice and help with completing claims forms. For the hard of hearing a text-phone 0800 243 355 is available (0800 243 787 for Northern Ireland).

There is also a helpline specifically for advice on the Disabled Living Allowance 0345 227 722 (local rate) for mainland Britain (0232 336 000 for Northern Ireland); or text-phone 0345 224 433 (local rate).

You can also get information from national organisations like the Carers National Association, Age Concern, Help the Aged, DIAL (the Disablement Information and Advice Lines) and, if the person you care for has a specific illness, from organisations and charities that represent them.

If you already have a social worker, he or she should not only be able to tell you which benefits you should apply for but also help you to fill out the forms. If you don't have a social worker you can phone the local social security office and ask for someone to help. Some areas have welfare rights workers who specialise in this sort of help. If a social worker can't give you the time needed then the local Citizen's Advice Bureau is also a good place to go for information and guidance.

It's important that you apply for benefits as soon as you can. Many are payable only from the date of application and can't be backdated. If you feel you've received less benefit than you should, then you need to take action quickly to appeal, as often the time in which an appeal can be lodged is limited.

The table at the end of the chapter lists most of the relevant allowances and benefits with brief details of how to claim and which forms to ask for. Remember that if your claim is turned down you can appeal. There are sample letters in this book to make this easier. Don't forget to use your local MP – he or she may well be able to take your case to a higher authority. Finally, remember – if in doubt, apply.

> All possible efforts have been made to ensure that the information on allowances, benefits and grants below is as up-to-date and accurate as possible at the time of publication. However, they are subject to change over time and it is advisable to check with the helplines and organisations above.

## Allowances, benefits and grants

### INVALID CARE ALLOWANCE (ICA)

You must be between 16 and 65 years old, and looking after a severely disabled person receiving either the Disabled Living Attendance Allowance (AA) Care Component at middle or higher rate, or Constant Attendance

Allowance (CAA), for at least 35 hours a week (Sunday – Saturday). You can be related or married, or no relation at all, to the person being cared for. You're eligible for ICA even if the period is only part of a year, e.g. school holidays. It's not means-tested but it is taxable and your earnings are taken into account. Payment of ICA credits you with Class 1 contributions for National Insurance (NI) purposes. If you have dependants, the ICA will be increased accordingly. Form DS700 DSS.

## CARER PREMIUM

This extra premium is paid if you're receiving Income Support (IS), other welfare benefit from the DSS or Housing or Council Tax benefit from the local authority. To qualify you must be entitled to receive ICA.

## HOME RESPONSIBILITY PROTECTION (HRP)

If you would normally be making NI contributions and are not because you're looking after a disabled person receiving either DLA, AA or CAA, and aren't claiming ICA, then HRP will reduce the number of years you need to meet the contribution conditions for retirement pension. The restrictions are quite complex but claiming is easy. Form CF411 DSS.

# Allowances for those cared for (over 65)

The criteria are all the same: severe disability either physical or mental and over 65 years of age. Note, for some over 65 but not yet 66 there may be special rules about which allowances to claim.

## ATTENDANCE ALLOWANCE (AA)

You don't have to have a carer but simply need one – how you spend it is up to you. It can be claimed on your behalf, it is paid at two rates either for day *or* night (lower rate) or for day *and* night (higher rate) The simple tests are i) Do you need help with personal care? and/or ii) Do you need someone watching over you to make sure you're safe? It's tax-free and not means-tested and it doesn't count as income when being considered for other benefits, which are earnings-related, e.g. Income Support.

You must have needed help for six months prior to claiming. The claim is not backdated, it's paid from receipt of your claim. DS702 DSS and claim form in DS2 booklet.

If you're diagnosed terminally ill (expected to die within 6 months) payment is not dependent on any tests, you will qualify at the higher rate but you must claim. If you survive longer than six months the allowance will continue to be paid. Kidney dialysis patients normally get the allowance at the lower rate.

# Allowances for those cared for (under 65)

### DISABILITY LIVING ALLOWANCE (DLA)

The allowance is divided into two parts: a Care Component and a Mobility Component. It's the main allowance for everybody under the age of 65. (There are special conditions for those aged between 5 and 16 and for those under 5.)

### THE CARE COMPONENT

This is paid at three different rates – higher, middle and lower. There are six basic tests which determine the level of disability, hence the level of payment.

For those who need care both day and night or are terminally ill the higher rate applies; for those who need help during the day or night or who require dialysis – the middle rate; and those who need part-time care or can't prepare meals for themselves – the lower rate.

The disability must have been present for three months prior to the claim and it must be expected to continue for six months after. It can be paid for life.

It's tax-free, not means-tested and does not adversely affect other social security benefits.

### THE MOBILITY COMPONENT

The allowance is paid at two rates depending on the degree of disability. At the higher rate the tests are: i) Unable, or virtually unable, to walk; ii) Deaf and blind; iii) Where walking would endanger your life or health. It is paid at the lower rate when even if you can walk you're so disabled, either physically or mentally, that you need guidance or help from someone else.

The allowance is tax-free and not means-tested, it does not affect other social security benefits. It may be paid to someone over the age of 65 provided that they're under 66 when they claim and have satisfied the disablement tests since before they were 65. To claim, ring 0800 882 200 (free) and ask for DLA 1 Claim pack. The allowance can be backdated to the date of your call.

### DISABILITY WORKING ALLOWANCE (DWA)

The claimant must be over 16 and working more than 16 hours a week. It's intended as an income 'top-up' for the disabled who are at a disadvantage in getting a job. It's tax-free but is means-tested. It's advisable to ask for detailed advice about this allowance as it may not increase the income of the disabled, the calculations are complex and are best done by specialists at the DSS. Details are on DS703 claim form in DWA 1 claim form pack.

### FAMILY CREDIT

This is a means-tested benefit for families on low wages. You must have children but can be either employed or self-employed. For a couple the award is paid to the wife who must make the claim. The award is normally made for a period of 26 weeks but is renewable. This benefit is a passport to other help, e.g. free prescriptions, glasses and dental treatment. For more information, see leaflet NI261 DSS.

### INCOME SUPPORT (IS)

This benefit was introduced to make sure that you have enough income to live on. If your earnings are low and you aren't working more than 16 hours a week, they're made up by this benefit to a minimum calculated on your needs, e.g. how many children you have. Disabled people and their carers get extra. These extras are called premiums.

**IS is one of the most important benefits for the low paid as it acts as a passport to many other benefits and allowances, from free school meals to help with your rent or mortgage.** Calculating what you're due is so important and complicated, that it's best for you to go through your claim with a DSS officer and to ask questions if you aren't absolutely clear.

The benefit is means-tested and depends on your earnings. Details are on IS1 DSS. A claim form will be sent when you have sent off the tear-off form on the back. (Complete NHB1 – see below – at the same time.)

### SOCIAL FUND (SF)

There are two parts to the SF: SF1 (mandatory) and SF2 (discretionary). If you get IS, DWA, Family Credit or certain local authority benefits, you may be entitled to money from the Social Fund. Some payments – maternity payment, funeral expenses and cold weather payments – are mandatory provided their criteria are met. Help under SF2 may be made either in the form of grants or as repayable interest free loans (maximum period 78 weeks). There are two types of grant/loan that may be made. You don't have a legal right to help from SF2.

The claim procedure is very complicated so ask for help from your social worker when making a claim and ask for a grant rather than a loan. For grants and loans use form SF300 DSS.

For Crisis Loans, which cover emergency help after a disaster, you use form SF400 DSS, which has to be filled in at the DSS office. Both grants and loans from SF1 and SF2 are means-tested. More details in leaflets SFL2 and SB16.

### HOUSING BENEFIT (HB) & COUNCIL TAX BENEFIT (CTB) (RENT REBATE IN NORTHERN IRELAND)

If you get IS, then these are benefits paid by your local authority. Complete form NHB1 at the same time as you claim IS as these benefits can't be backdated earlier than the date of your claim. Housing Benefit: rent rebate if you live in a council house and pay rent; rent allowance if you live in other rented property. Council Tax Benefit: this benefit is paid as a relief from some or all of your council tax (in Northern Ireland, you can get a rent rebate to help with your rates). More details on leaflets RR1, RR2 & CTB1. Form NHB1 is used for both these benefits.

### CONSTANT ATTENDANCE ALLOWANCE

This is an allowance paid to those getting industrial injuries disablement benefit and is a passport to ICA.

### ORANGE BADGE SCHEME

This is a national arrangement of parking concessions for disabled or blind people – either drivers or passengers. Holders can park free in many car parks and on single yellow lines for limited periods to allow easy access to shops etc.

In England and Wales you can get full details and forms from your local authority social services department; in Scotland apply to the chief executive of your Regional Council; in Northern Ireland to The Registrar, Hydebank, 4 Hospital Road, Belfast BT8 8JL. There is a small fee and the badge is awarded for a maximum of three years. You then have to re-apply.

Your GP can support your application but there is no appeals procedure if the request is turned down.

# Appeals

When you claim a Social Security benefit all the relevant information regarding your claim will be assessed by an independent Adjudicating Officer (AO). The AO's decision should be reported to you within 14 days after getting all the information.

If you don't agree with the decision you can ask for it to be reviewed. An explanation of the decision in writing this review will be made by the AO. You must ask for this information within three months (see Letter 1).

If you don't agree with the adjudication, then you may appeal but the appeal must be lodged within three months of the original decision having being made.

You must now decide to whom you should appeal, this will depend on the nature of the appeal.

If you need help, try the freephone numbers for the Benefits Agency 0800 882 200 and Social Security 0800 666 555. Your local Citizen's Advice Bureau may be helpful or able to suggest a law centre, or legal firm in the area who will give you either free advice or advice under the Green Form scheme (legal aid). If you're on IS, DWA or FC you will automatically qualify but the cost of legal aid is limited by your income and savings.

- *For decisions made by the AO, which don't involve medical or disability decisions, appeal to a Social Security Appeal Tribunal (SSAT), also for appeals involving points of law (see Letter 2).*
- *For decisions involving medical matters made by an Adjudicating Medical Authority (AMA), appeal to a Medical Appeal Tribunal (MAT) (see Letter 3).*
- *For decisions concerning disability regarding DLA, DWA and AA appeal to a Disability Appeal Tribunal (DAT) (see Letter 4).*
- *If your appeal is late it may still be heard provided your explanation of delay is accepted by the tribunal chairman (see Letter 5).*
- *If you're dissatisfied with the verdict of the tribunal you may appeal to a Social Security Commissioner. You can only appeal at*

***this level on a point of law. The Commissioner can't deal with
medical matters.***

Not only the AO but all tribunals and commissioners are independent of
the DSS.

It doesn't matter to which tribunal you wish to appeal, all letters should
be sent to your local office who will deal with them as appropriate.

In the back of leaflet NI246, there's a form which may be used but you
don't have to use it. For convenience there are sample letters at the end of
this chapter.

If you really hit a brick wall your MP may be able to help. Your MP can,
in extreme cases, raise questions in the House of Commons. Find out the
name of your MP from your local library, then write to him or her at the
local office or at the House of Commons, London SW1.

Remember to keep copies of all your letters.

# Housing grants

There are five grants available, only three will really concern you as a carer:
Renovation, Minor Works and Disabled Facilities grants.

Housing grants are made by the local authority. It's normally the
Environmental Services Department which deals with these improvement
grants. Get the booklet *House Renovation Grants* from your local authority.
After you've read it, a letter to your local authority asking for help and
advice would be a good place to start (see Letter 6).

Some grants are 'mandatory' which means that the Authority *must* make
them. Others are 'discretionary' which means that the Authority *may* make
them if it decides to – but it doesn't have to.

# Renovation grants

**Owner occupation** (If you own the dwelling, even if you have a mortgage,
you're the owner). Unless the dwelling is classified as 'unfit for human
habitation' any grant is discretionary.

Discretionary grants may be paid for work such as repairs which,
if not done now, will require greater expenditure in the near future.

Mandatory grants are made to bring the dwelling up to habitable standard and can cover heating, lighting, ventilation, damp proofing, water supply (hot and cold), kitchens, bathrooms, toilets and drains, and must be approved by the local authority in advance.

Both types of grant can include the cost of professional fees, such as architects' and engineers' fees.

They are means-tested and the savings and income of all those who live in the property are taken into account. If the owner decides to sell the property within three years then a proportion of the grant will be taken back.

**Tenants** (If you pay rent). You should check the tenancy agreement to find out whether you or the landlord is responsible for the works you feel necessary. If your landlord is responsible then a letter to him explaining the situation is the first step. In the last resort the courts can force him to do the work. If it's your responsibility then provided the dwelling is your main residence, and you intend to remain there the rules are as for owner-occupiers (see Letters 7 and 8).

# Minor Works grants

These grants are discretionary and are not available to council tenants. They are available to owner-occupiers and private tenants. They are to cover the costs of small works up to about £1000. (For major works see Disabled Facilities grants below.)

They're means-tested in so far as you must be receiving: Family Credit, Disabled Working Allowance, Council Tax Benefit, Housing Benefit or Income Support.

You can make several applications, up to a maximum of three in three years, and there's a maximum grant made per application. They can cover the costs of both materials and labour and can be made as:

**Thermal insulation grants:** to cover the cost of loft and cold water tank insulation and draught proofing.

**Staying put grants:** for owner-occupiers/tenants over 60, to enable them to remain in their own homes, e.g. basic improvements or adaptations including safety measures.

**Elderly residents adaptation grants:** for those over 60, to enable them to live in the dwelling. e.g. an extra toilet, shower, heating or even a kitchen.

**Lead pipe grants:** to cover the cost of replacing lead pipes used to supply drinking or cooking water.

## Disabled Facilities grants

When major works have to be done, e.g. building an extension for a disabled person, this is the grant to apply for. It's mandatory and means-tested, the only conditions are that the works that the disabled person requires are reasonable, practicable and agreed as being necessary by the authorities. There are no restrictions on who can apply for or receive a Disabled Facilities grant. (Landlords may apply on behalf of a disabled tenant.)

Grants will be made towards any cost associated with enabling the disabled to have access to, and within, a dwelling, to provide room for sleeping, facilities for bathing, improving the heating system, to enable the preparation of food and the adaptation of heating and lighting controls, etc.

## VAT

Even if the disabled person doesn't qualify for any of the these grants, it's important to remember that certain works and provisions for the disabled are zero-rated for VAT. Works associated with accessibility, providing a bathroom or toilet, lifts and hoists, alarm systems and extending or adapting a dwelling to accommodate any of these are all zero-rated.

You must have the work done by a VAT-registered builder. Contact your local VAT (Customs & Excise) Office for details before starting any work.

# Sample letters

Remember to keep copies of all letters you send. You should also keep notes of any phone conversations, including the date and time of the call, and who you spoke to. If anything is agreed or offered over the phone, ask for it to be put in writing. Write a letter confirming your understanding of the conversation.

---

**LETTER I – Asking for reasons for rejection or removal of benefit**

Your reference [found at the top of their letter]

If there is no reference then put name of person being cared for.

Date

Address (include postcode)

Social Security Number and/or National Insurance Number

Dear Sir,

I am looking after.......................[name of the person being cared for] and am writing on her/his behalf.

We have just received notification from your office that our request for ............................... [give details of benefits] has been turned down.

I find it difficult to understand how this has been decided and would be grateful if you could send me details of how this decision was made, and on what grounds the claim was rejected.

[Sign and date the letter and send it to the office which notified you of rejection.]

---

**LETTER 2 – Appealing against the AO's decision. Use letter 3 for an appeal against a medical ruling**

Your reference [found at the top of their letter]

If there is no reference then put name of person being cared for.

Date

Address (include postcode)

Social Security Number and/or National Insurance Number

Dear Sir,

I am looking after ........................ [name of the person being cared for] and am writing on her/his behalf.

We wish to appeal against the Adjudicating Officer's decision not to award/to withdraw ............................ [give details of benefits claimed].

The reasons for this appeal are ........................ [give as much detail as possible as to why you think the benefit should be paid]

(e.g. Given her/his level of disability and the amount of care I have to give, which your office do not question). The more information you give the more likely it is that the appeal will be allowed.

[Sign and date the letter and send it to the office which notified you of rejection.]

**LETTER 3 – Appealing against a medical ruling**

Your reference [found at the top of their letter]

If there is no reference then put name of person being cared for.

Date

Address (include postcode)

Social Security Number and/or National Insurance Number

Dear Sir,

I am looking after ..................... [name of the person being cared for] and am writing on her/his behalf.

S/he wishes to appeal against the decision of the Adjudicating Medical Authority who have decided that s/he is not/no longer to be classified as ................................. [say here what disability is being challenged].

As a consequence s/he is no longer receiving ........................ [name of benefit withdrawn or withheld].

S/he has been seen by ..............................[give consultant's and doctor's names] who do not agree with the verdict of the Adjudicating Medical Authority. I enclose letters from them which support our view.

It is on the basis of this evidence that we are asking for this appeal to be allowed.

[Sign and date the letter and address it to The Clerk to the Medical Appeals Tribunal and send it to the office which notified you of the decision. They will send it on.]

**LETTER 4 – Appealing against decision that the person cared for is not entitled to DLA, DWA or AA**

Your reference [found at the top of their letter]

If there is no reference then put name of person being cared for.

Date

Address (include postcode)

Social Security Number and/or National Insurance Number

Dear Sir,

I am looking after ................. [name of the person being cared for] and am writing on her/his behalf.

S/he wishes to appeal against the decision of the Adjudicating Medical Authority who have decided that s/he is not/no longer to be classified as ...................... [say here what disability is being challenged].

As a consequence s/he is no longer receiving .................. [name of benefit withdrawn or withheld].

I am looking after her/him and can testify that s/he needs constant attention during the day and at night and is incapable of looking after her/himself. S/he is not capable of walking any distance.

I have kept a diary during the past month which details the help I, and others, have had to give.

On the basis of this evidence we feel that the appeal should be allowed.

[Sign and date the letter and address it to The Clerk to the Disability Appeals Tribunal and send it to the office which notified you of the decision. They will send it on.]

---

**LETTER 5 – If your appeal is late add this to your letter of appeal**

I realise that this appeal is late but this is due to ...................... [give your **special** reasons for delay].

(e.g. documents from the local office were late in coming etc.)

We appeal to the chairperson to permit this appeal to be heard and also ask that the appeal be allowed.

**LETTER 6 – Asking for help with an improvement grant application**

Name of person being cared for

Date

Address (include postcode)

Social Security Number and/or National Insurance Number

Dear Sir,

I am looking after ........................ [name of the person being cared for] and am writing on her/his behalf.

S/he is receiving .................................... [give names of benefits] and believes that s/he is eligible for a grant towards improving the dwelling in which s/he lives.

[Give details of particular problems with the dwelling.]

As s/he is incapable of travelling to your office would you please arrange for a member of your staff to come and give advice as to which grant s/he may qualify for and how s/he must proceed.

[Sign and date the letter and send it to *Head of Environmental Services* at your local authority council offices.]

**LETTER 7 – First letter to the landlord requesting that works be done**

Name of person being cared for

Date

Address (include postcode)

Dear Sir, [Use the name if you have it]

re repairs at above address

I am looking after ................................ [name of the person being cared for] and am writing on her/his behalf.

The property that s/he rents from you is badly in need of repair.

[Give details of defects.]

We have examined the tenancy agreement and are convinced that these repairs are the responsibilitx of the landlord.

[Give reference to the section of the agreement.]

Would you please, therefore, arrange for the work to be carried out as soon as possible.

[Sign and date the letter and send it to the landlord at the address on the tenancy agreement.]

**LETTER 8 – Strong letter to landlord**

Name of person being cared for

Date

Address (include post code)

Dear Sir, [Use the name if you have it]

re repairs at above address

I am looking after ........................ [name of the person being cared for] and am writing on her/his behalf.

I wrote to you on ........................ [give date] giving details of repairs to the above property that s/he believes it is your responsibility to put right.

If the work is not started within the next 14 days s/he intends to take legal advice and if necessary s/he will commence proceedings against you for an injunction ordering you to carry out these repairs, and damages for your failure to repair.

Even if the work is commenced within the next 14 days s/he reserves the right to claim damages for your failure to repair.

For your convenience I enclose a copy of my original letter which gives details of the necessary repairs.

[Sign and date the letter and send it to the landlord by *registered post*.]

## ALLOWANCES AND BENEFITS WITH FORMS NEEDED

| Allowances and benefits | Brief details | Leaflet No. | Use Form No. |
|---|---|---|---|
| Attendance Allowance | Must be over 65 and severely disabled. Day or night or both. Not means-tested. Tax-free. Simple test. Note: each person in a household eligible for benefit. | DS702 | DS702 |
| Child Benefit (Family Allowance) | Each child under 19 in full-time secondary education (up to A level) eligible. Not means-tested. Tax-free. There is a single parent benefit in addition. | CH4 CH4A CH5 CH6 & CH7 | Coupon in leaflet FB8 |
| Community Care Grant | A grant which may be paid to those leaving institutional or residential care to help them lead independent lives. Means-tested. | SFL2 & SB16 | SF300 |
| Council Tax Benefit | Must be over 18 and liable to pay Council Tax. Means-tested on a sliding scale. There are exemptions if living away from home, either being cared for or caring for someone. If in doubt claim. | CTB1 | NHB1 |
| Disability Living Allowance | Tax-free – not means-tested. Not affected by income. Must be claimed before 66th birthday and must have become eligible before 65th birthday. Two components: Care and Mobility Tests. | DS704 | DLA1 Claim pack |

| Allowances and benefits | Brief details | Leaflet No. | Use Form No. |
|---|---|---|---|
| Disability premium | Additional allowance for those on Income Support or Housing Benefit. Only paid while the recipient is under 60. | IS1 | Form in IS1 |
| Higher Pensioner premium | Paid if you have received the Disability premium, are still disabled and over 60, or if you are over 80. | IS1 | Form in IS1 |
| Severe Disability premium | Paid in addition to the Disability premium for those on IS living alone, and who receive the DLA above the lowest rate. *Note* No one must be receiving ICA for looking after you. | IS1 | Form in IS1 |
| Disability Working Allowance | Must be over 16, disabled and working more than 16 hours per week. Tax-free but means-tested. Normally of limited duration (26 weeks) – intended as an income top-up for the disabled who are at a disadvantage in getting a job. A key to other benefits. | DS703 | DWA1 |
| Disabled Child premium | Additional premium for those on Income support or receiving Housing Benefit, if child is receiving Disabled Living Allowance or is blind. Means-tested on a sliding scale. | IS1 | Form in IS1 |

| Allowances and benefits | Brief details | Leaflet No. | Use Form No. |
|---|---|---|---|
| Family Credit | Income-related benefit as a supplement for those on low incomes with children. Means-tested relative to capital. Passport to other benefits. | NI261 | Claim Pack FC1 |
| Home responsibilities protection | Protects pension rights of a carer while not contributing while looking after someone for more than 35 hours per week for 48 weeks a year. Those cared for must be receiving the Attendance Allowance. | CF411 | CF411 |
| Housing Benefit | Help with rent if on low income or Income Support. Means-tested. If in doubt claim. | RR1 & RR2 | NHB1 |
| Income Support | For those not working more than 16 hours a week. Intended to make sure you have enough to live on. Means-tested and depends on your earnings. Acts as a passport to other benefits and allowances. | IS1 | Form in IS1 |
| Industrial Injuries Disablement Benefit | A benefit paid to those who have been injured at work or have an industrial disease. It is paid in addition to any National Insurance benefit you may get. The amount you receive will depend on how badly injured you are. | NI6 NI2 NI3 NI7 NI207 NI272 NI237 | BI100 series |

| Allowances and benefits | Brief details | Leaflet No. | Use Form No. |
|---|---|---|---|
| Invalidity Benefit | Paid when Statutory Sick Pay runs out (after 28 weeks). It is tax-free and premiums for children etc. are paid. | NI16A | Normally auto-matic |
| Invalid Care Allowance | Must be of working age up to 65 looking after disabled person for more than 35 hours per week and earning less than £50 per week. Not means-tested but taxable and earnings-related. Some other benefits affected. | FB31 | DS700 |
| Severe Disablement Allowance | A tax-free allowance for those who have not been able to work for 28 weeks but are not eligible for Invalidity Benefit (not enough  contributions). Premiums are paid for dependants. | NI252 | Form SDA1 in NI252 |
| Sickness Benefit | Benefit paid in lieu of Statutory Sick Pay if your employer can't pay it. *Or* if you are self-employed or unemployed *but* you must have paid NI contributions. Tax-free. | NI16 & NI253 | |
| Statutory Sick Pay | Paid by your employer for the first 28 weeks off sick. | NI244 | |
| Unemployment Benefit | Paid for the first 12 months after being made unemployed. You must have paid NI  contributions. Not means-tested but taxable as income if you have other income | IR41 | |

In the Budget of November 1993 several changes to the benefits listed above were announced:

♦ *From April 1996 unemployment benefit will become a 'Jobseekers Allowance' which will only be non means-tested for 6 months after which it will become a means-tested benefit.*
♦ *From April 1995 Invalidity and Sickness Benefits will become an 'Incapacity Benefit' which will require a medical test. The benefit will also be taxed.*
♦ *There are also planned changes to the qualifying conditions and entitlement to Family Credit, Disability Working Allowance and Housing and Council Tax Benefits.*

*Make sure you ask for and get the latest versions of the leaflets.*

# 6

# MAKING LIFE EASIER

Many carers can fall into the trap of doing too much for the person they care for. We all have a lazy streak and the more you do for the person you care for, the less they may want to do, or feel capable of doing, for themselves. It's not easy to be patient and stand back while someone slowly gets dressed or feeds themselves but it's worth it. There are also ways of making your life easier – often quite simple to organise or arrange – that can make a tremendous difference.

## Personal care

For some carers, particularly children looking after their parents or older relatives, washing, bathing, dressing and taking someone to the toilet are a natural part of their caring role. Others may find this the hardest part, very aware of the private nature of these functions.

> *"I could feel the irritation rising as I watched my mother fumbling to put on her clothes or wash. I had to be there in case she fell but mostly I wished myself miles away. Usually I'd end up snatching the things and helping her. This made her cross too and we'd end up shouting at each other."*

This carer found it impossible to be patient, partly because she didn't feel comfortable doing these personal things for her mother. The answer was to ask social services for a home sitting service to come in twice a day to help her mother bathe and dress, while she got on with housework, shopping and cooking and caring for her disabled mother in other ways.

It may not always be so easy to get this sort of help, so here are some suggestions:

◆ *If you're caring for someone who's confused you may get cross if they don't co-operate. If so, it may help to walk away while you recover your composure (provided it's safe to leave the person alone).*

- *Understanding how the other person feels helps. It can be upsetting to have to be helped with these private things. Talking together about it may ease the embarrassment. Sometimes you can laugh together about the absurdities of the situation. Others have found that being as matter-of-fact and kind about the help you're offering can make a difference.*
- *There are also aids to dressing and bathing that allow the person cared for to do more. For women there are front-fastening bras, and tights and stocking aids to help get these items on. There are also button hooks and zip pullers.*
- *Choose clothes that are easy to put on – pullovers with wide necks; loose rather than tight sleeves; slip-on shoes rather than laces or buckles. Remember that the way we dress is very personal, so allow the person you care for to have their say.*
- *You can get special seats for the bath to ease getting in and out, and grab rails for extra support. You can have seats for the shower. There are raised seats and rails for toilets.*
- *You can buy adjustable beds.*
- *If going to the toilet is a problem you could think of hiring a commode.*
- *You can get armchairs that can tilt up and allow a person to stand up more easily.*
- *Make use of the personal care services available in your area. Chiropody (care of the feet) is vital for people with conditions like diabetes. Pensioners and registered disabled can have free treatment under the NHS. You can refer yourself or go via your GP or health visitor.*
- *For a list of qualified chiropodists in your area (they must have SRCh after their name) write to The Society of Chiropodists.*

# Incontinence

This is one of the more difficult things to deal with. People are naturally embarrassed at having accidents. It helps to know that it's very common among people of all ages – not just the ill or elderly – and it can either be managed discreetly or successfully treated.

Incontinence can be caused by medical problems like an enlarged prostate in men or a bladder infection. Stress incontinence occurs when weakened pelvic floor muscles mean that laughing, sneezing or coughing can cause leaking. Often with an older person it can simply be due to not reaching the toilet in time.

Cutting down the amount drunk is not the answer and may be dangerous as it's important to drink enough fluids each day. If the incontinence occurs at night then you could avoid drinks in the evening, especially tea, coffee and alcohol.

Simpler clothing fastenings and maybe a commode will prevent accidents in some cases where mobility is a problem.

You could try keeping a diary for a while to see if any pattern emerges.

Ideally the GP should be the first person to talk to but if the person you care for finds this too difficult, then through the district nurse you should be able to see a trained Continence Advisor.

For leaflets and advice contact the Continence Foundation.

Social services can provide incontinence pads and most areas have a laundry service – especially important if you're dealing with faecal as well as urinary incontinence.

# Dental care

Good dental care is important because problems with teeth and gums can affect eating habits. The person you care for should visit the dentist regularly, even if he or she has dentures, as these need checking too. Some dentists will visit a person at home and most social service departments have a list.

# Hearing and sight

Make sure you get the best aids for sight and hearing. DIAL (Advisory Committee on Telecommunications for Disabled and Elderly People) on 071 634 8700 has information on telephone services for the elderly, the disabled and their carers. The RNID and RNIB have information on the latest developments.

# Around the home

If you share a home with the person cared for, try to involve them in the daily routine. Although you may be doing quite a lot of caring, you may still be able to find areas in which the person you care for retains some independence. There are hundreds of gadgets and aids on the market now that can make this possible. They range from large items, like lifts and stairlifts to simple gadgets like kettle tippers which allow you to pour boiling water without having to lift the kettle and mesh baskets to insert in saucepans to make draining vegetables easier.

*"My mother can no longer cook a meal but she can help by preparing vegetables so it makes her feel useful."*

*"After his second stroke my father couldn't get upstairs. We put a bed for him in the dining room and he had to use a commode. It was awful – for him and for us. After a lot of thought we put in a stairlift. He still needs help with dressing and going to the loo but the fact that he can go upstairs like the rest of the family made a tremendous difference."*

Your occupational therapist (see Chapter 4) is the best person to talk to about increasing or maintaining independence and other carers may also have ideas. For large items such as lifts, ramps and alterations to the house to make life easier you may qualify for a Disabled Facilities grant to help with costs (see Chapter 5 for details on how to do this). Medical and nursing equipment can be provided through the health authority

Smaller items you may have to buy or get on loan. Or you may be able to apply for a grant.

## WHERE TO FIND OUT MORE

Some gadgets are available in ordinary mail order catalogues, others in large pharmacies. For more information, contact: The Disabled Living Foundation; The Disability Information Trust; At Disabled Living Centres; RADAR (The Royal Association for Disability and Rehabilitation); Keep Able; Homecraft Chestercare Nottingham Rehab Ways and Means; Boots the Chemist; Age Concern. For addresses, see Chapter 10.

# Safety at home

Carers often spend a lot of time worrying about the safety of the person they care for. There are more likely to be accidents if you, the carer, are tired, under pressure or angry. Of course no one expects you not to suffer these emotions at some point – you may have an argument with the person you care for or have had a difficult day at work – but making the home as safe a place as possible can help avoid disasters.

## TAKING CARE OF MEDICINES

◆ *Pharmacists sell tablet boxes with clearly marked compartments for each pill to be taken over a week. You can keep track of what has to be taken and when.*

◆ *Keep a daily timetable of what pills need to be taken and when. On a record card write details of the drugs, what they're for, what the dosage is and when they were prescribed. This will help you ensure that there are no unnecessary repeat prescriptions and pinpoint adverse reactions.*

◆ *When the doctor prescribes medication for the person you care for, ask what the drug is for, what side effects there are, if any, and if the drug might interact with any other drug or with alcohol. If you cannot get this information from the GP, then the pharmacist who dispenses the medicine will be able to help and will also confirm the correct dosage.*

**"My mother-in-law has Alzheimer's Disease but her confusion seemed to be getting worse. We were desperate and were even thinking of finding a residential place for her when, by chance, I began to wonder whether some pills she'd been prescribed might be affecting her and giving her hallucinations. I talked to her GP,**

*she stopped taking them and the change in behaviour was amazing."*

◆ *Some side effects of drugs are unavoidable but if they're making life difficult you should talk to the GP. Often an alternative drug may suit the person better.*

◆ *Always keep drugs in a safe place, ideally a locked medicine cupboard.*

◆ *Some medicines need to be taken with meals. If the person you care for is unwell and not eating properly, a couple of biscuits is an acceptable substitute.*

## MAKING THE HOME SAFER

◆ **Good lighting** *is vital. If the person you care for gets up at night make sure corridors and stairways are well lit.*

◆ **Clear floors** *so that nothing is left around to be tripped over. As well as toys this will include trailing flexes, small items of furniture, newspapers. Make sure stair carpets fit well and get rid of any mats on tiled or wooden floors.*

◆ **Wear sensible shoes.** *Shoes with rubberised soles and low or no heels make sense both for the carer – especially if you're having to do any lifting – and for the person cared for to lessen risks of falling.*

◆ **Extra support** *may be needed for an older or disabled person to hold onto. You may want to install an extra rail up the stairs, grab rails in the bathroom and by the toilet, a rail alongside garden or front door steps.*
*Help the Aged has a booklet* Safety in Your Home *available free from their headquarters.*

◆ **Smoke alarms** *should be installed in any room where there's a risk of fire starting. This will include the living room, the landings on each floor, outside, not inside, the kitchen and bathroom. If you or the person you care for smokes then you must be extra careful about stubbing out. Try not to smoke in bed. When buying a smoke alarm choose one with British Standard Number BS5446 and the Kitemark.*

◆ **Appliances** *like gas fires, cookers, central heating should be checked regularly to make sure they're not leaking. British Gas will carry out a free safety check on appliances if the person you care for is*

*over 60, living alone or with someone else over 60, is registered
disabled and living alone, or is receiving a state disability benefit.
Its Home Service Advisors will visit you at home.*

*Electrical equipment should be checked regularly and your local
electricity showroom can provide a list of qualified people. Some
electricity boards will visit your home to advise you. But you can
keep an eye on things such as worn flexes and not overloading
power points or using the wrong fuses in plugs. The Electricity
Association has a number of booklets and leaflets including* **Advice
for Elderly People.** *These are available from some electricity shops
and libraries and from Electricity Publications, Robert Guy
Services Ltd, 54-62 Raymouth Road, London SE16 2DF.*

◆ *Keep heaters away from curtains, furniture and bedclothes. Put
guards on all open fires, fill paraffin heaters outdoors and don't
sit close to fires.*

◆ *Never use an electric blanket with a hot water bottle.
Underblankets should be switched off once the person you care
for gets into bed – although some newer versions are specially
low voltage and safe to sleep on – check the instructions.*

◆ *In the kitchen, if a fat fire starts, turn off the heat at once and
cover the pan with a lid or damp cloth and leave for at least
30 minutes. If you want to buy a fire blanket look for products
bearing British Standard Number BS6575. You can also buy
cooker guards to prevent saucepans being tipped over.*

◆ **Keeping warm** *is important. See Chapter 5 for information on
allowances and grants you may be entitled to to help with heating
and insulation costs.*

*For advice on keeping warm in winter there are freephone lines:
England and Wales 0800 269626 (0800 289404 for text); Scotland:
0800 838587. Northern Ireland: 0800 616757 (you can also get
information on benefits on this number). Age Concern Scotland
have a book on hypothermia and how to avoid it, available from
54A Fountainbridge, Edinburgh, EH3 9PT. There's also a free
booklet with advice on clothes, heating, food.*

◆ *If the person you care for is disabled, the local authority, under the
Chronically Sick and Disabled Persons Act, has a duty to provide
or help certain disabled people to get a phone. People on Income
Support may be able to get a loan from the Social Fund for this
(see Chapter 5). British Telecom (Freephone : voice – 0800 800 150;*

*text – 0800 243123) has a free guide for disabled and elderly people with lists of the latest products. DIAL has an information pack on telephone services for disabled and elderly people.*

◆ *If the person you care for lives alone, or if you have to leave him or her alone and are concerned that they may not be able to call for help using the phone, then a community alarm could be the answer. You need a phone line with a plug-in socket and a 13 amp power point nearby. The user either presses a special button on the phone or on a pendant. This alerts staff at the control centre who can speak to the person and find out what help is needed. There is a wide range of alarms to choose from. Before deciding contact Help the Aged's Community Alarms Department at head office.*

## WHAT TO DO IN CASE OF FIRE

◆ *Close all internal doors.*
◆ *Get everyone out of the house.*
◆ *Call the fire brigade.*
◆ *Don't go back into the house.*

If you're trapped in the house, go to a room that's not affected by the fire – preferably one overlooking the street so that the fire brigade has easier access to you and you can open the window and call for help. Close the door and block it with anything you can find – furniture, bedding, clothes – if there is water available in the room dampen them.

## PERSONAL SAFETY

If the person you care for lives alone, remind him or her of the Association of British Insurers "knock" code:

◆ *Know your caller.*
◆ *Never allow entry without identification (keep the chain on the door. All public service employees have to carry identity cards.*

*If they say they've left their card at home ask them to call back another time).*

◆ *Open the door only when you're satisfied that the caller is genuine.*

◆ *Call the police (by dialling 999) if you're suspicious.*

◆ *Keep an eye on any caller while he or she is in the house. (In other words, don't leave them alone in a room while you fetch something, or standing at the open door, always leave the chain on.)*

## Caring for the home

There are changes and improvements you can make to the home where you do your caring that will make life more comfortable and easier. For some alterations you may be able to get grants – see Chapter 5 for further details. There are some organisations and groups who can offer advice and help (see Chapter 10 for addresses).

Anchor have a 'Staying Put' service which aims to help older home owners improve and repair their houses so that they can live there more comfortably. They advise on the work, on choosing a builder to do the job and on technical aspects. They can also offer financial advice and help you to apply for grants. Care and Repair Ltd is a friendly society which has been chosen by the government to be the national co-ordinating body for all Home Improvement Agencies. They develop and support Care and Repair projects in all parts of the country. If the alterations you wish to make increase the size of the house or if the house is listed you may need planning permission. Contact the planning department of your local authority for advice or get a free copy of *Planning: A Householder's Guide* from Department of the Environment, PO Box 135, Bradford, West Yorkshire BD9 4HU or phone the Public Enquiry Unit on 071 276 0900.

## Getting through the day

Some sort of routine can make life easier and less stressful.

◆ *A basic routine for the person you care for may involve getting up and going to bed at the same time, having a bath every night, taking pills, exercise and meals and the same time and so on.*

*Around and amongst these points in the day you may be able to create little oases of surprise. Remember that you need a break each day – you may not go out but you must have time for yourself.*

◆ *A bedtime routine may also be essential, especially if the person you care for is confused or has sleep problems. A person with dementia may wake in the night and wander. They may also be difficult towards the end of the day, just when you're tired too. Try to remain calm and be vigilant about possible safety hazards – this may mean stair gates and bars over upstairs windows and locking back and front doors.*

◆ *Don't wait until you're totally exhausted before seeking help. Night sitting is available is some areas but you need to be persistent. If social and voluntary services can't help then think of alternatives – getting a member of the family or neighbour to stay the night occasionally is one option.*

◆ *Create your own carer's diary. Apart from listing things you do each day you can also note dates to remember, points you may want to raise with social services, any changes in the condition of the person you care for, questions you want to ask. With so much on your plate it's easy to forget things or write them down on pieces of paper which then get mislaid. It can also provide a reliable record if you want to pinpoint an event or a change later in the year.*

◆ *If you spend much of your day with the person you care for it can be hard to find things to do to pass the time. Apart from the time for yourself you need to include things that are enjoyable in each day. These can be quite simple and need to suit the person's capabilities. They could include going for a walk, having a friend in for coffee or tea, visiting someone together.*

◆ *Exercise each day is good for both of you. The person you care for may not be able to do more than a few stretches but a specific time – as little as ten minutes – set aside for this is a good idea. If you're not sure what exercises are appropriate ask the community physiotherapist for advice or write to Extend. Some day centres also offer exercise classes – check in your area.*

◆ *Caring for someone with a deteriorating condition can be frustrating and depressing. Concentrate on the things the person can do, look for ways to simplify activities to bring them within his or her grasp. Having a hairdresser visit the house to do someone's hair or an aromatherapist or reflexologist to offer a massage can make a lot of difference to a day.*

♦ *Depending on his or her physical and mental abilities there are a range of activities to choose, from learning at home through the Open University to jigsaw puzzles and needlework projects. If there is a day centre for the person to visit then encourage them to do so – being with other people is stimulating and community care has given rise to improved programmes at these centres offering more than basket work.*

## Friendship and companionship

If you have always had a good relationship with the person you care for, you'll find it easier to keep talking. In some cases you'll have to simplify conversation: speaking more clearly, dealing with one subject at a time, helping the other person find a word.

Often, following a stroke, impaired speech can be improved and The Stroke Association has local groups which can offer advice. Talk to your GP about speech therapy.

If your relationship with the person you care for has never been close or if you really don't get on well, you may find it hard to talk. There are other ways to show that you still care – a hug, a cuddle, holding hands, giving a gentle neck and shoulder massage with soothing music in the background. Sometimes the person cared for can be very unkind or even abusive. If this upsets you either leave the room if it's safe to do so or make sure you have someone to whom you can let off steam.

> **"My father-in-law used to call me the most terrible names and although I knew it was part of his dementia it didn't stop me from feeling really upset and angry. The first time I confided what I felt to someone at the local carers' group I felt really embarrassed and disloyal – but it did help me see I wasn't alone and that I wasn't doing a bad job caring."**

Tell social services if the abuse is too overwhelming. You may feel the time has come to stop caring or alter the amount you do (see Chapter 9) or you may be able to have extra help provided to take some of the pressure off.

A pet can be a wonderful companion. Animal Aid offers support to older people by using local volunteers to take dogs for walks or feed a pet if its owner is ill or in hospital. If money is a problem the PDSA may be able to help. Look in the phone book for your local branch or contact head office.

# Keeping on the move

Get out of the house once a day if you can. Even within the home the more you can help the person you care for to be mobile the better.

A physiotherapist or occupational therapist will advise on the sort of equipment needed – walking frames, trolleys and wheelchairs can make a lot of difference. Sometimes these can be loaned or provided by social services – ask your social worker for advice or contact the British Red Cross Society.

If the person you care for drives and has a disability or if you need to take that person in your own car they may qualify for an Orange Badge allowing them parking concessions. You apply for the badge through social services (for details see Chapter 5).

Disability Network Information Services has information on disabled parking facilities in over 200 authorities of Britain. Send a SAE.

For details on transport for disabled people both for local and long distance journeys the Department of Transport publishes *Door to Door*, a very comprehensive guide.

# Getting a break

Frequent short breaks from caring are vital for carers – however much they love the person they care for. Talk to your social worker about respite on a regular basis. She should be able to arrange a sitting, visiting or nursing service. Sometimes a day care centre won't suit the person you care for. There may be residential homes and nursing homes which can look after someone for a couple of weeks.

An alternative is adult placement schemes – sometimes known as family link schemes. The person cared for goes to stay with a "foster" family, either for a few hours a day or week, or on a longer term basis. Ask your social worker if there's a scheme in your area – sometimes it will be run by social services or other organisations.

Carers also need holidays. Social services, voluntary agencies, your GP, district nurse or health visitor should be able to organise respite care and most social services departments and libraries have copies of the *Charities Digest* which gives more information on organisations offering respite care.

Some authorities will offer the person you care for a place in a local authority, private or voluntary home or in hospital via the District Health Authority. Voluntary organisations may also be able to help – again, ask your social worker or local carers' group. Private care is also available. It's expensive but allows you, the carer, to go away, while the person you care for remains at home. It's always worth asking.

RADAR publishes an annual holiday guide for disabled people while the Holiday Care Service can help people with mobility problems find a suitable holiday as well as give advice for those on low incomes.

Tripscope can help you plan any trip – either everyday or a holiday, local or long distance.

Money is often the main bar to carers getting a break. There are some trusts to approach who give grants towards the cost of a holiday. The best source of information is *The Directory of Grant Making Trusts* published by the Charities Aid Foundation – most libraries have a copy.

Age Concern also publishes information (Factsheet No. 4) on holidays for older people, including details of trusts and grants.

If the person you care for has a specific illness you can get holiday and respite advice from the relevant charity.

## What to do in an emergency

In spite of careful planning accidents can still happen, things do go wrong, people fall ill unexpectedly. It helps to have planned in advance what you can do. Ask yourself the following questions:

◆ *If there is an accident or illness or care crisis, who do I contact?*
◆ *What is their phone number?*
◆ *Are they contactable 24 hours a day?*
◆ *If not, who can I contact at any time?*

When you have the answers to your questions write them down and keep them somewhere safe. Remember that there is someone on duty in social services 24 hours a day. Make sure you have the correct number.

You can phone your GP's surgery at any time as well. You will either be given a special number for calls outside surgery hours or your GP may have special instructions on the usual number.

To call an ambulance dial 999 and ask for the ambulance service. This can be done for free from a public phone box

If it's a medical emergency and your GP can't get to you quickly enough then either call an ambulance or, if it seems sensible, take the person you care for to the accident and emergency department of your nearest hospital.

If you have no phone then see if neighbours would agree to your using their phone in an emergency. Make sure you know where the nearest public phone box is and keep coins and/or a phone card to hand

It can help to discuss your plans for a crisis or emergency with your GP, health visitor, district nurse and any helpers involved with the person you care for.

Keep a list of contact names and numbers by the telephone and make sure others involved in caring also have relevant numbers.

You might want to learn basic first aid techniques. If you can find the time both St John Ambulance and the British Red Cross Society run courses (addresses in your local phone book).

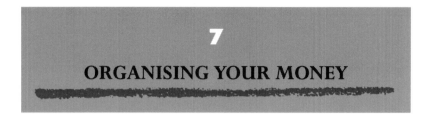

## Money and legal matters

As a carer you may often worry about money – both your own and that of the person you care for. Many carers are short of money – you may have had to give up a job in order to care or work part- instead of full-time; as an older carer you may have lost out on full pension rights; as a younger carer your career may never have got off the ground and you may be unsure about what benefits you're entitled to (see Chapter 5 for all information on benefits and remember that the golden rule is, if in doubt, claim).

Managing your money is an important part of caring. Because you may have less money than you might have had, it's all the more important that you use what you have efficiently.

If caring takes up most of your time or you share a home with the person you care for, you should think about discussing finances before resentments build up. In any case, it's always embarrassing to have to ask anyone for money and if things are organised in a business-like manner from the beginning, it can make everything a lot easier.

If you're caring for a person with dementia it can be difficult to know when you should take over. Sometimes people with dementia can lose all idea of the value of money. Before that stage is reached it might be better to have a discussion about the future when the person you care for is still able to make decisions.

What will help you most is to have a clear idea of your own financial situation. If you can complete the tables that follow you will know where you stand. Remember to refer to Chapter 5 to make sure you've included all the benefits you are entitled to. With this strategy you'll be in a better position to plan on a weekly or long-term basis.

You can use the same tables to calculate the assets and income for the person you care for, if this is appropriate.

**WHERE TO START : A STRATEGY**
Completing the following tables will help you to prepare an overall picture of your financial situation.

# Working out your assets and income

## ASSETS

It's important to complete this table first as some benefits are dependent on the amount of savings that the person you are caring for has.

| Assets | Value |
|---|---|
| House | |
| Car | |
| Bank accounts | |
| Stocks and shares | |
| Building society accounts | |
| Life assurance policies | |
| Major items in the house, e.g. jewellery, silver, etc. | |
| TOTAL | |

## INCOME

It's simpler to reduce the amounts to weekly or monthly values

| | Taxable | Non-taxable | Weekly / monthly amount |
|---|---|---|---|
| Salary/wages if still paid | | | |
| Pension from work | | | |
| *Welfare benefits:* Use Chapter 5 and the DSS booklets to decide what *welfare benefits* you and the one you are caring for are entitled to | | | |
| Investment income | | | |
| TOTAL | | | |

You should also try and estimate how this position will change in the near future, e.g. How long does the salary continue? Will there be a lump-sum on retirement as part of any retirement pension?

## INCOME TAX

Once you have done this you must find out what tax is due on this level of income. A phone call to the Inland Revenue inspectors (number in the phone book) is a good idea as they will do all they can to advise you how much is due, and what extra tax allowances may now be available; but a letter will be safer and will stand as proof of consultation if anything goes wrong in the future (see Letter 9). Your local tax office is permitted to send an inspector to see you at home but whether or not they will is a decision for them to make and will, of course, depend on the number of staff available.

---

**LETTER 9 – To the Inland Revenue on behalf of the one being cared for**

Name of person cared for

Date

Address (include postcode)

Dear Sir,

I am looking after ..................... [name of the person being cared for] and am writing on her/his behalf. S/he is aged ..............

I am trying to work out her/his available income and have prepared the figures on the attached sheet(s).

Would you please check that I have included everything I should and advise me if I haven't.

From this information would you please tell me the amount of tax s/he would be likely to pay and whether there is any way that this amount can be reduced.

[Sign and date the letter and send it to the Chief Inspector at the local Inland Revenue office (it's in the phone book).]

---

If you wish to clarify your own tax position as a carer you can use the example, left, as the basis for a similar letter, giving details of your own savings, benefits and income. Remember to include your age as the allowances you are eligible for may be greater if you are over 60.

There are many excellent books for advice, notably *Which? way to save tax* from the Consumers' Association, and *Your taxes and savings* from Age Concern.

If you discover there is no liability for tax, it's important that you look carefully at any savings accounts where tax is deducted automatically, since you may be able to claim the tax back. Or you may find that the money would be better invested where interest is paid gross (i.e. is not taxed before it's paid).

# What are the debts and outgoings?

**DEBTS**

| *Creditor* (to whom the debt is owed) | *Amount* |
|---|---|
| Mortgage | |
| Bank overdrafts | |
| Hire purchase | |
| Credit cards | |
| Council tax/rates | |
| Water | |
| Gas | |
| Electricity | |
| Others | |
| TOTAL | |

**OUTGOINGS**

| Expenses | Amount | Frequency (how often paid) | Reduce to weekly or monthly amounts |
|---|---|---|---|
| Mortgage/rent | | | |
| Council tax | | | |
| Water rates | | | |
| Insurance policies | | | |
| Gas* | | | |
| Electricity* | | | |
| Oil etc.* | | | |
| Housekeeping | | | |
| Food | | | |
| Clothing | | | |
| TV licence | | | |
| TV rental | | | |
| Travel/car | | | |
| Car insurance | | | |
| Medical costs | | | |
| Medical insurance | | | |
| Newspapers | | | |
| Cigarettes | | | |
| Alcohol | | | |
| Entertainment | | | |
| Others | | | |
| TOTAL | | | |

*Remember to allow more for these utilities than in the past as the house may now need to be heated for longer each day.

If you now find that income is less than expenditure you must try and reduce the expenditure. From the expenses table pick out the items that are no longer needed or may be reduced. DON'T cut down on the heating or the food, although you can reduce the heat in the rest of the house and keep only the rooms used up to the usual temperature.

In some cases, it may be very difficult to adjust the expenditure to fit the income and professional help may be needed – try your social worker first. If you can't manage, DON'T BORROW ANY MONEY, it will only make matters worse.

Most bills can be paid on a weekly basis, even the electricity and gas bills, but you must arrange this with the boards. (You can even pay them at the post office using a GIRO cheque.)

If there is some major debt that must be paid you should contact the creditor (the one who is owed the money) and try and arrange to pay it off weekly in small amounts. It's always a good idea if you make the first approach rather than waiting until they approach you.

# Acting on behalf of someone else

Most benefits are paid on a weekly basis by means of payments books from a local post office. On the back of each counterfoil there is an authorisation that the person receiving the payment may sign, giving someone else authority to collect it on their behalf. Although this method may continue as long as you and the one you care for wish, it is better to formalise the arrangement.

Involvement in another's affairs can be at several levels. At the lowest a simple informal collection of welfare benefits, at the highest, it may require the carer being given legal powers to make decisions and manage completely all financial and personal aspects of another's life.

It is essential that all authorisations and powers of attorney are granted before the one you are caring for becomes mentally incapable.

### AUTHORISED AGENCY

When the informal collection of welfare benefits becomes a permanency, the local benefits agency will issue an identity card to the collector so that they may be identified at post offices and may receive the benefits. The Authorised Agent must hand over all the payments to the beneficiary.

## APPOINTEESHIP

To operate someone else's bank account, or collect benefits on a permanent basis, a letter from the account holder to the bank or benefits office is often sufficient. But when the one you care for is no longer capable of dealing with welfare payments themselves, the Benefits Agency will appoint someone to both *receive* and *administer* the benefits on another's behalf.

A visiting officer will normally visit and decide whether an appointeeship is appropriate. The agency must be convinced that the appointee is acting 'in the best interests' of the claimant.

## POWERS OF ATTORNEY

There are two different sorts of Power of Attorney: an Ordinary Power of Attorney and an Enduring Power of Attorney.

An Ordinary Power of Attorney is given by one person (the donor) who gives to another (the attorney) the legal authority to manage their affairs. A power of attorney may be given for a limited period, and for very specific purposes. A legal deed has to be drawn up, normally with the help of a solicitor (at a cost of between £25 and £100), but special forms are available from: OYEZ Stationery Ltd, 49 Bedford Row, London WC1, if you want to do it yourself.

To save a lot of argument later it would be best to consult the family members of the person you care for.

An Ordinary Power of Attorney can't cover major transactions and would be automatically cancelled if the donor became mentally incapable.

## ENDURING POWER OF ATTORNEY (CONTINUING POWER OF ATTORNEY IN SCOTLAND)

Because an Ordinary Power of Attorney is automatically cancelled if the donor becomes mentally incapable then it may be advisable to consider an Enduring Power of Attorney. You may use forms available from: OYEZ Stationery Ltd, 49 Bedford Row, London WC1.

Because the powers granted may be very significant and because other family members *must* be advised that an Enduring/Continuing Power of Attorney is being given, it's recommended that the donor takes legal advice from a solicitor.

The powers granted may be general, or specific and contain restrictions. A donor can even make more than one Enduring Power of Attorney with different Attorneys having different powers and can specify the conditions which must apply before the powers become effective. Enduring Powers of

Attorney must be registered with the Court of Protection. (There is a fee, £50 in 1994.)

As long as the donor remains mentally capable, Enduring/Continuing Powers of Attorney may be revoked (cancelled) but this cancellation will only take effect once the Court of Protection has confirmed the cancellation. The court may cancel the power if the Attorney proves unsuitable. The Court of Protection is called the Office of Care and Protection in Northern Ireland. It doesn't exist in Scotland – there is a more expensive and difficult procedure to go through.

If someone is found incapable then the Court of Protection can appoint a receiver, normally from among family members but quite possibly from a firm of solicitors, the local authority or even voluntary groups. Fees will be charged to cover the court's costs.

More information about Powers of Attorney is available from the Public Trust Office (Stewart House, 24 Kingsway, London WC2B 6JX, telephone 071 269 7000). Ask for the free booklets *Handbook for Receivers* and *Enduring Powers of Attorney*.

Your local Citizen's Advice Bureau (number in the phone book) is often the best place to start when seeking legal advice.

# Making a will

A will is a legal document that sets out how the Estate (property and possessions) of the person making it is to be divided up when they die. It may set out the arrangements he or she would like for their funeral and eventual disposal of their body. If there are children under 18 the will may outline how they are to be brought up and even request a particular person to do it. The will should also name the person or persons who are to see that its instructions and requests are carried out, they are called executors and are said to execute the will.

The person making a will must be capable of understanding what he or she is signing and their signature must be witnessed by two people who are not going to receive anything from the estate.

When someone dies without making a will they are said to have died 'intestate' and their property and possessions will be divided up between their relatives. There are very specific rules that determine how much each member will receive. These rules are complicated and there's no guarantee that a particular family member will get a particular possession. The legal costs in dividing up such an estate will certainly be greater than the cost of making a will.

If there are no relatives and a person dies intestate then all the property, etc., will go to the Crown (the State).

In any relationship where partners are not married, which includes gay and lesbian partners, making a will is the only way that they can inherit from one another

Making a will is the only way that you can guarantee your wishes are respected.

## WHAT TO DO

A will can be written on a form that can be bought from many stationery shops with advice from many very good books on the subject. But it's not as easy as it sounds, it's quite possible to say something in a will that does not mean what it appears to say. After death no one can say what was intended only what the document means in strict legal terms. In the worst case the will could be invalid, and it could be held that the person died intestate.

Solicitors make more money sorting out a badly written will than they do from writing one. Many will now draw up a simple will for about £50, a complicated one will obviously be more expensive.

Before seeing a solicitor it's best to make careful notes of possessions, etc., and decide who should inherit what. Saving a solicitor's time will certainly save money. The local Citizen's Advice Bureau can provide a list of suitable local solicitors.

# Where do you (the carer) stand?

Before you, the carer, give up your own home to go and live with and care for someone, it's really important that you both consider where you will live if they die. If the one you're going to care for owns their own home then it may be possible for them to make detailed arrangements in their will which will allow you to stay there. However, if they have a family who are expecting to inherit the house there could be all sorts of repercussions and it would be best to involve them in the discussions before any final decisions are made.

If the house is rented it's often possible to take over the tenancy on their death of the person cared for but it would be better for you both to become joint tenants; you then become the surviving tenant. Contact your local Age Concern (number in phone book) for advice.

# BEREAVEMENT

There may come a time when your role as a carer reaches a natural conclusion and the person you care for dies. For so many carers the death of the person they care for is a real watershed. For some it will mean a release from an overwhelming commitment of both time and emotions, for others it can bring devastating loneliness and fear. Very often there will be a bewildering mixture of emotions.

> *"Caring for my mother had become almost full-time towards the end of her life. Some days she barely recognised me, others she was so rude and bad tempered. I can admit now that there were days when I wished her dead. But when it finally happened instead of the great relief I had expected I felt totally lost and grief-stricken. It has taken me a long time to sort out my feelings."*

## Preparing for death

Often carers think about the death of the person they care for. You may have done this – wondering how you will cope, what will happen. Knowing that death is imminent means that you have a chance to discuss some things if you wish, make some preparations. Even if the person you care for is healthy, if they are quite elderly then thinking about what might happen when they die is not really morbid but may help put your mind at rest and solve some anxieties. The person you care for may also be worried about what will happen to you when they are gone, so talking together may help them too.

Of course not all of us can be so practical. If you feel that the idea of thinking and planning for death is not for you, maybe because it's too painful or frightening, then do what feels most comfortable. There may still be one or two things that you can sort out, to set your mind at ease, leaving others to be dealt with as the need arises. Here are some of the things which you will probably want to consider:

**SHOULD THE PERSON I CARE FOR BE TOLD THEY ARE DYING?**

These days the attitude seems to be to give people as much information as possible, or as much as they wish. As carer you may be the first to be told but no health professional would expect you to be the one to tell the patient. If this should happen you should gently but firmly insist that the health professional does this. It may help if you are there so you can remember exactly what has been said. Certainly if you are asked directly then you should tell the truth. There may be details to be discussed, the person may wish to make arrangements, preparations or even be reassured that you can take care of things for them.

Often elderly and very ill people do know when they are dying but they may prefer not to acknowledge this and will not want to have such information forced on them. By listening carefully you may get some clues and it may help to talk to the doctor or a sympathetic nurse about this.

**WHERE SHOULD THE PERSON BE CARED FOR?**

The alternatives are discussed in more detail in Chapter 9 but if you wish to care for a terminally ill person at home then you can get a lot of support – both day and night.

Start by talking to your GP as he or she should know about the availability of local services. Your social worker, district nurse or hospital nurse may also be helpful.

At home you can have extra help. There are Home Care Teams and Hospital Support Teams – these are trained nurses. There are also Macmillan nurses who can offer help to people with cancer and their families. Some areas have a Hospice at Home group who can help. Generally these services are free.

**IF THE PERSON GOES INTO HOSPITAL HOW INVOLVED SHOULD I BE?**

This will depend on the relationship and how open you can be with each other. If the person you care for has dementia you may have to make many decisions on their behalf, including some about treatment and how much doctors should intervene to prolong life. If there are special requests to be made regarding care then you can either talk to the hospital team or, if you prefer, to your GP who will pass your wishes on.

*"When my husband was finally admitted into hospital I knew that I didn't want anything extra done. I just wanted him to be comfortable and not in pain. The nurses were truly wonderful. They made me feel that I was part of the team. During those last three*

*weeks – I was there, at his bedside, helping. When the end came I felt I had completed the job properly and that was a comfort."*

Hospices are well used to patient's relatives, friends and carers being at hand, hospitals may be less flexible. You'll be under a great deal of strain and worry at this time and you may be anxious that everything is being done the right way. It's hard for a carer to let go, even a small amount. If you can work with the hospital staff it will help you as well as them. Talking to the staff, showing you value what they are doing rather than feeling resentful should help you through this difficult time.

## HOW CAN I DEAL WITH OUR FEELINGS?

Some people are relaxed about death and approach it with calmness and acceptance. Others alternate between denial, anger and depression as well as periods of acceptance. As a carer this will put you under additional strain because you'll also have your own feelings to cope with. You both need support at this time and there are people who can offer this.

Again you can talk to your doctor, who may be able to direct you to support groups. Your carers' group may prove a tremendous source of comfort and if the person you care for is suffering from a specific illness such as cancer there are often local support groups.

## IS THERE ANYTHING PRACTICAL THAT I CAN DO?

There are some documents and information that you will need when the person dies. In particular, you should know where the following are:

♦ *the will (if there is one)*
♦ *birth certificate*
♦ *marriage certificate*
♦ *medical card*
♦ *National Insurance card*
♦ *bank details and savings books (building society, post office, etc.)*
♦ *insurance policies*
♦ *welfare books (e.g. disability allowance, pension)*

Give the person you care for the chance to see relatives and friends. Knowing we only have a limited time left does give us the opportunity to say goodbye, to express feelings of love or regret. Often a person who seems to have no religious beliefs may feel a need to see a priest or minister at this stage.

Sometimes the person may no longer be able to hold a conversation but your presence may still be appreciated. You can talk gently, hold hands, give a gentle massage, read favourite prayers or poems.

*"Two things brought my father peace in his last few days. One was the grandchildren visiting each afternoon. They didn't stay long but they often brought a drawing or piece of work they'd done at school. Then we moved the hi-fi into his room and played his favourite music. When he died Chopin was playing and I'll always be glad of that."*

## Living wills

A 'living will' is a written statement giving details of how the person making it wishes to be treated if they are very ill and may be about to die. It's essential to discuss the matter with a doctor before making one. More details and a form, which is legally acceptable, are available from: The Terrence Higgins Trust (see Chapter 10). Although the Trust is a charity specifically for those with HIV its services are open to everyone and the living will form is suitable for anyone wishing to make one.

## What happens when someone dies

However prepared we are for death it often takes us by surprise. If the death occurs in a hospital or hospice there will be nurses and doctors to help you. But as a carer you may be anxious about how you will react if the death occurs at home when you are the only one there.

If this does worry you then rather than pushing it to one side, it will help to find answers to some of your questions. You'll never know exactly how you'll react until it happens, but if you have some idea of what to expect and what you should do, it may help ease feelings of panic.

*"I knew that my mother was going to die but I was terrified of the actual death. One day at the doctor's he mentioned my mother's possible death and I simply burst into tears and was able to tell him how I felt. He was very reassuring – he couldn't guarantee that she*

*would die quietly in her sleep but by explaining what I should do he took away some of the fear. He also suggested that I should get a night nurse in if I really didn't want to be alone and not to feel that this was a sign of failure."*

- *If the death happens at home then the GP is the first person to contact. Find out beforehand what the procedure is if death occurs in the middle of the night and whether your GP can come straight away.*
- *If the GP's seen the patient recently and the cause of death is clear, he'll be able to give you a Medical Certificate showing the cause of death. You must take this to the Registrar's Office to register the death.*
- *After you've phoned the GP, you may want to phone family and friends or a neighbour who may be able to come and be with you. You can also phone the funeral director and start making arrangements.*

### HOW TO TELL IF SOMEONE HAS DIED

There are simple checks you can make, if you wish, to establish that the person you have cared for has died. Please don't worry if you can't do them – simply phone your GP and wait until he or she arrives. The checks are:

- *Feel for a pulse, either at the wrist using two fingers (not your thumb which has a pulse of its own) or inside the arm by the elbow.*
- *Using a mirror check for breathing.*
- *Look at the eyes to see if there is any movement or reaction.*

## Seeing the Registrar

The death must be registered within five days. You don't have to make an appointment. Simply take the Medical Certificate signed by the doctor, the deceased's medical card, birth certificate and marriage certificate. You'll have to tell the Registrar:

- *the date and place of death*
- *the deceased's address; first names and surname (and maiden name if relevant); the date and place of birth*

- *the deceased's occupation and, if relevant, the name and occupation of her husband*
- *the date of birth of the deceased's surviving widow or widower*
- *whether the deceased was receiving a state pension or other benefit.*

The Registrar will give you the following:

- *A Death Certificate – which you'll need for the will and any insurance policies, savings bank certificates, premium bonds and pension claims.*
- *Certificate of Registration – to send off with any pension or welfare books when you return them.*
- *Certificate for Burial or Cremation – which you have to take to the funeral director.*

## Planning the funeral

The funeral is the final farewell – although in some cases people do organise a memorial service a month or so later if many people have been unable to attend the funeral or if the person was particularly well known – often the funeral is the only chance people get to say their goodbyes.

This does not mean that the funeral has to be a sad, solemn occasion – often people ask to be remembered with laughter rather than tears, for their life to be celebrated.

If you've already discussed this with the person you care for, it's much easier to organise. If not, it will have helped if you have thought about what might be appropriate. Funerals have to be arranged quite quickly at a time when you're not in the best state to make decisions. Here are some of the things you might need to think about:

- *burial or cremation*
- *type of service – religious or secular (non-religious)*
- *what hymns, music or readings*
- *what sort of memorial or headstone or where the ashes will be scattered*
- *what the person would like to be dressed in.*

In many cases the funeral director can be helpful here, especially if there hasn't been an opportunity to think about these things. Most funeral directors are kind and understanding and can guide you well.

If you or the person cared for is closely involved with the local church, synagogue, temple or mosque then someone will probably visit and be able to offer advice and guidance on funeral arrangements.

Although you are the carer there may well be other people who wish to be involved in the decisions over the funeral – other family members for instance. This is why forward planning can help.

*"When my father died my mother and I had a row over whether he should be buried or cremated as no one had thought to ask him – it was so unnecessarily upsetting at a time when we should have been comforting each other. Afterwards, my mother sat down and wrote out instructions for her own funeral – we even discussed the hymns she would like."*

Finding out how much a funeral will cost is something else we may put off. It seems morbid and distasteful to walk into a funeral directors and ask for a price list but it does make sense to get two written estimates, preferably in advance. Funerals are a business like any other and as a customer you're entitled to have something that you can afford.

However distressed you are, try not to let yourself be talked into spending more money than you planned. If you feel pressurised, try and find someone, another family member, a friend, a neighbour, to be with you when these decisions are made.

The basic cost of a funeral will include removal, a hearse, coffin and the director's fees. On top of that there will be extras such as crematorium fees, doctor's fees, minister's fees. There may also be items such as organist, church fees, extra cars, announcements in local or national papers.

If you're not related to the person you care for, you should be careful about getting involved in funeral arrangements – there may be family or distant relatives to take on this responsibility.

Check whether the person you care for has taken out a funeral plan. These allow you to plan and pay for your funeral in advance at current prices or to take out a special insurance policy to cover funeral costs.

# When the funeral is over

It's often after the funeral that the grieving really begins. As a carer you may be so busy with practicalities in the days leading up to the funeral that there will be little time for reality to sink in. You may go through these days in a state of numbed shock, almost of disbelief.

> **"After the funeral breakfast was the worst time of all – suddenly I was on my own for the first time in over 20 years of caring. The temptation to run away was very strong. Some friends stayed behind to help wash up and one offered to stay the night. My daughter had suggested going away for a few days but I'm glad I didn't. It would have been harder to come back."**

There are various well-recognised stages of bereavement – you may experience some or all of them, in stages or recurring bouts:

- *Shock and disbelief – 'this can't have happened', 'surely I'll walk into the room and she'll be there as usual'. A sort of numbness can get you through the first few days.*
- *Anger – either that the person has died and left you alone, or that after years of caring you feel there's nothing to show for your devotion. You may also feel angry at the way other people try to comfort you.*

> **"So many people came up to me and said, 'Well, it's a happy release. Now you can live your own life again,' after my mother died. It really made me mad. I felt it was an insult to me and my mother and it sort of took away any value of what I'd done for her and the love I'd received in return."**

- *Open grief – you may weep for hours, get to a stage when you feel you have no more tears and then weep again.*
- *Depression – although this will underlie much of your sadness it can last a long time and be accompanied by a feeling of total apathy. You may have made plans for your future life but haven't the energy to do anything. Some carers feel suicidal at times, wondering whether life is worth living.*
- *Gradual acceptance – this is when recovery begins. Although you'll still have times when you need to grieve, these will be less frequent.*

Alongside these feelings you will have others that will depend on how you saw your role as a carer, your relationship with the person you cared for, the sort of life you led and the kind of life you envisage now. You may feel bitter, guilty, frightened, self-pitying, lonely or relieved.

These are all very normal emotions and although you may feel that you should ignore them, it's best to allow yourself to express them either to yourself, a close friend or a counsellor. They're part of the grieving process.

Try to call on the strength that helped you to care so that you don't let others push you around and force you to make decisions before you're ready. People are well-meaning – though it has to be said that sometimes the advice offered is more for their own peace of mind than yours – but you need time, once you have dealt with the urgent practicalities, to get used to this new way of life.

It may take you longer than you expected to recover from the sharp sense of loss. You may be extra sensitive to other people and the way they avoid the subject of your bereavement. If depression or lack of sleep are really bothering you, see your GP. Often a carers' group can offer you the understanding support you need at this time.

Many carers suffer physically while they're grieving as the immune system is less resistant to infection. You may get a lot of minor illnesses such as colds and flu or you may be quite seriously ill. You may find you're very accident prone for a while, or in pain from strained muscles after years of lifting.

This is a time to put yourself first and not feel guilty. Allow yourself small treats that will comfort you. An occasional day or two away may help, or a trip to the theatre or cinema, or an evening with friends. You may need to learn how to give time to yourself again.

Only too often for carers, friends have been lost if the caring has been demanding. If you've never been to a carers' group, now might be a good time – you may no longer be a carer but you have something to offer in return for the companionship – experience of caring. On the other hand, you might find it upsetting to hear other people complaining about their situation when you've just lost the person you've been caring for.

You still have a lot of life ahead of you or you may have children who still need you – but you may be able to work round their needs and still find time for yourself.

## Occupying the time

If you're used to a routine, then life may seem both empty and purposeless. Days can drift by and if you find this depressing you may want to find one or two things to do each week at a specific time to begin to bring some structure back into your life – an evening or day class, a regular walk or coffee with friends are possibilities.

Quite a number of carers are tempted to take on another caring role but before you commit yourself, think carefully. Is this what you really want to do? Or is it an easy option, safer perhaps than trying something different? Is it what others expect of you? Families are very good at casting one member as caring: 'Eileen will do it, she did such a wonderful job looking after Dad'. Before you decide, try and discuss it with someone objective.

Although you may no longer be actively caring you can still give time in practical ways. You could go to local groups to pass on what you've learnt, do some voluntary work, or even campaign for improvements in conditions for carers.

You may find comfort in simply sitting quietly at home going through old photographs or letters, talking about the person you cared for with family and friends.

No one can tell you how long the grieving lasts. Even when you feel your life is almost back on an even keel, a piece of music, a time of year, the sound of a voice can trigger a wave of sadness – accepting this and understanding it will help you.

## Coming to terms

For some carers the grieving takes place long before the person they care for has died.

> **"Although I was sad when Jim died, it was nothing compared to the pain I'd gone through three years earlier when he'd had his stroke. That was when I said goodbye to the man I'd married – the loving husband and father. He couldn't speak and was very confused most of the time. Coming to terms with that was far more painful than his death."**

When this happens it can help to have specialist counselling to help you mourn the person you knew and loved. It will allow you to continue to value them.

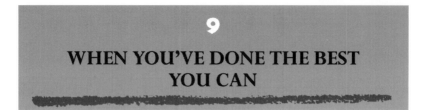

The time may come when you decide to change your caring role. For many carers the decision to stop caring arises because the person they care for needs more help and support than they can provide.

An illness like Alzheimer's or Parkinson's Disease, a stroke or a major operation may call for enormous amounts of care. In terminal stages, cancer and AIDS patients for instance, may need specialist nursing.

Sometimes you may have to stop caring through your own ill health or because the person cared for no longer wants you to do the job. Or, quite simply, you may feel you've done enough, that the demands on your time and energies, however great or small, are too much. If the care you give is affecting other areas of your life such as your family or your career, or if the relationship with the person you care for deteriorates, it may be a happier decision for everyone if you re-organise the caring.

Even if you feel the decision is a positive one you may still be surprised to go through a variety of emotions. Amongst them may be relief, guilt, a feeling that somehow you've failed. These are normal but it's best if there's someone in whom you can confide.

**WHAT ARE THE OPTIONS?**

There are three main options:

◆ *more support for you, the carer*
◆ *residential/nursing care home*
◆ *sheltered accommodation.*

## More support

Before handing over care completely you could consider asking for more help and support. If you feel you're at the end of your tether, this could be an answer. See Chapters 4 and 6 for advice but remember to be as strong and firm as you can be when you ask for help. You might point out that the alternative is that you'll have to withdraw from your role as carer.

Since the introduction of community care and the closure of many local authority residential care homes, the emphasis is on providing more care at home. Often an authority will provide a great deal of support to a person living alone, especially as it's still cheaper than residential accommodation. In some cases, it could be 24 hours a day, 7 days a week and come from a variety of sources. However, if there's a carer around, this sort of support is rare. Most carers find they have to struggle on until there's a crisis, and either their own health is at risk or the person cared for needs very special care.

Once you've seen social services you should also approach local groups such as Age Concern or Community Service Volunteers (CSV). The advice these days to carers is to think ahead and begin to ask for extra help well before it's needed. That way, there's time for something to be arranged. You may also have more strength to insist on what's needed.

> **"It was a friend at the carers' group who told me to ask for a night-sitting service for my husband. At that stage the disturbance at night wasn't too bad. I felt I could cope. But as the weeks went by I became more and more exhausted. Because my request was already in and there had been an assessment, it was easier to go back and tell them that things had got worse. I now have a sitter three nights a week."**

## OTHER THINGS TO CONSIDER

◆ *Before deciding that a care home is the only alternative, remember that it's quite a major step. If the person you care for has their own home, they'll probably have to sell up or give up their tenancy in order to move into a care home. If things don't work out it may be very difficult to move back into the community.*

◆ *If you share a home with the person you care for, make sure of your rights before they move out (see Chapter 7).*

◆ *If you've managed to care until now without having any close contact with social services, think about asking for their help. You may also want to ask them to produce an assessment of needs (see Chapter 4).*

◆ *Make use of the voluntary organisations which offer good advice to carers in this situation. Age Concern, Carers National Association and Help the Aged can all help and guide you.*

◆ *If you know you can no longer be a carer, discuss this with the person you care for. Obviously they have a role to play in making the decisions.*

◆ *If you've not done so, contact the GP and ask (if appropriate) to have a proper medical assessment of needs carried out. At the same time, make sure that any drugs being taken are the right ones and are not making a person's condition worse. Sometimes a change in drugs can make a great deal of difference. For instance, some drugs can cause incontinence, confusion, hallucinations, depression. These can often be the final straw for a carer.*

◆ *If the person you care for has dementia, ask for a specialist consultation, if this hasn't already happened.*

◆ *If there is time to consider the options make full use of it. Try not to be hustled into making a final decision. In some cases, if you feel you have reached the end of the road, well-organised and regular respite care may help. At least it will give you a better chance to think calmly about the future.*

## Residential care homes

◆ *In a residential home the person will get all meals and some personal care (i.e. help with bathing, dressing and feeding). The amount of care offered will vary from home to home. Often it may be no more than you're doing at the moment.*

◆ *Some residential homes won't accept people with medical conditions that need additional or specialised care (like Alzheimer's Disease, diabetes, epilepsy or severe confusion). Other homes are specially registered to provide care for such people.*

◆ *There are local authority (sometimes referred to as Part III) homes; voluntary homes run by non-profit-making bodies (like charities, religious groups or housing associations); and private homes run by individuals or companies as a business.*

◆ *All residential care homes, even those with fewer than four residents, have to be registered with the local authority. An inspector visits once a year to check that the home is being run properly.*

# Nursing homes

◆ *Nursing care is provided by qualified nurses and auxiliary staff 24 hours a day. A qualified nurse is always on duty.*
◆ *All nursing homes must be registered with the district health authority and are inspected twice a year. You should be able to see the certificate of registration which has to be displayed prominently.*
◆ *Some homes offer both residential and nursing care. The idea is that as residents need more care they can receive this without the upheaval of a further move.*

# Sheltered housing

You and the person you care for may want to consider this option if the sort of care you give is mainly to do with providing companionship.

These flats, bungalows and sometimes houses are available to buy or rent. They're usually unfurnished and there may be a communal laundry, sitting or dining room. The accommodation is specially adapted for older people with lifts and ramps to make access easier.

Services will vary but the best developments are those that are near shops and other local facilities, rather than in the middle of nowhere with only an occasional local bus service. There will be an alarm system and a warden on site for reassurance and emergencies. Wardens won't provide daily help or any care.

Some sheltered housing groups, like Anchor, realised that residents often have to move once they need more care and are setting up schemes where this is provided.

Before entering into any commitment, always check the small print for extras. Apart from the purchase price or rent, there will be service charges to cover the provision of the warden, laundry, alarm systems and maintenance.

Local social services and branches of Age Concern have information on schemes in your area. Age Concern also runs an advice and conciliation service on 071 383 2006.

You could also consider the sort of sheltered housing provided by schemes like the Abbeyfield Society. Housing for small groups of older people is provided in large family houses adapted or purpose-built to give residents their own room. A resident housekeeper offers support while a house committee of volunteers organises outings, visits the home and raises funds. There are now extra care houses which offer 24-hour personal care.

## Who pays for care homes?

If the person you care for is assessed, and social services agree that residential or nursing accommodation is suitable, they may pay some of the costs – following a financial assessment. Put simply, at the moment, if the person you care for has more than £8,000 in capital and savings, he or she will have to meet the full cost of the fees. This may mean selling the home they live in, in order to get the money. If you, the carer, live in the home of the person you care for permanently then, depending on circumstances, the local authority may ignore the value of the dwelling. (See Chapter 7 for more information on your housing rights.) If the person has less than £8,000, the local authority will assess their ability to pay. Total income will be taken into account – including benefits like Income Support, pension payments and so on – and the local authority will pay the remainder of the fees.

Counsel and Care for the Elderly can offer advice on a variety of subjects and could be useful for grants to support older people in care homes. Charity Search offers a free advice service to help older people who have real financial difficulties find a charity that may be able to help them. A book, *Charity Made Clear,* gives extra details. Your local Citizen's Advice Bureau may also be able to help if money is a problem.

## Finding a home

Your local authority will have a list of registered care homes in the area (go to the district health authority for nursing home lists). If the person you care for is to go into a Part III (local authority home) there may be only one to choose from. If you don't like this home, you can make your own suggestions – even for a home in another part of the country. There should be no problems over this provided that the local authority feels the home you choose is suitable, the home agrees to have the person cared for, has a vacancy and the cost is not more than the authority would usually pay (although it's sometimes possible to get help with the extra costs).

If the local authority is not going to fund residential or nursing care, then once you have a list, you can approach the home yourself and make your own arrangements. (See Chapter 10 for organisations like the Elderly Accommodation Counsel who can help you in your search.)

## MAKING A GOOD CHOICE

It may be quite hard to find the right home but don't be tempted to jump at the first place that has a vacancy unless there's a crisis and accommodation has to be found at once. If possible, visit and compare several homes, preferably with the person you care for. Both of you will have your own ideas of what would be suitable and what's important, so make a list. We will all have different priorities but here are some ideas:

◆ *Does the home have a warm, relaxed atmosphere? When you visit, talk to both staff and residents and try and get a feel of whether the home matches up to the claims in its brochure.*

◆ *How independent are residents – despite disabilities? Are they encouraged to do things for themselves? Can they choose how they spend their days, prepare simple drinks or snacks, see visitors at any time, use the telephone?*

◆ *If there's a routine, how strict is it?*

◆ *Is the home clean? Are there any unpleasant smells?*

◆ *If the person has special needs – either physical or mental – would the home cater for these in a way that seems right to you?*

◆ *If the person's condition is likely to deteriorate and need more care, can the home provide this or would the person have to move elsewhere?*

◆ *Is there a proper complaints procedure? If a resident is unhappy how can they discuss this, and with whom, without fear of repercussions? Is there a residents' committee?*

◆ *How are the days spent? Are there plenty of activities, outings, stimulation, volunteers coming in?*

- *How like home is it? Can residents bring their own possessions or small items of furniture? Can they have a single room? Are there several living rooms (so you don't have to watch TV if you prefer to read or chat)? Can you have meals in your room, have visitors to stay?*
- *Look at the weekly fee and see what it covers. There will be extra charges for essentials like chiropody, laundry, hairdressing and physiotherapy.*

## MAKING THE DECISION

Even after the choice of home has been agreed, it's still a good idea, if there's time and circumstances make it possible, to have a trial stay of a few days or weeks. Most homes should agree to this as it gives both the home and the future resident a chance to see whether things are going to work out well.

Of course, if the person you care for has negative feelings about going into residential care it may be hard for them to see anything good at all. If you've discussed it with them (if this is possible) and feel at ease about the choice of home then you must allow yourself to relax and hope that things will settle down, given time.

If you know you've done what you can to make a good choice, you should try not to let feelings of guilt take too firm a hold. It will help to talk to others in a similar situation and maybe see a counsellor.

Often everything is easier once the move has been made.

*"I used to lie awake at night worrying how an outsider could possibly cope with my mother. I was used to her ways and had made so many allowances for her over the years. I knew that if she was unhappy she could be even more demanding. But I underestimated the care staff and their ability to adapt to all sorts of people. I visited regularly, always unexpectedly, and was reassured to find Mum well and happy."*

## MOVING IN

Any move is disturbing and a move from one's own home into residential care can be a very emotional time. Even if the home doesn't allow a resident to bring their own furniture there should be room for some personal possessions – photographs of family and friends, a radio, books and so on.

As a carer, you'll have mixed feelings and for lifelong partners of any sex, seeing their loved one go into residential care can be heart-rending.

*"The decision was made for me in the end because I was so tired, both mentally and physically. Joan, who has Alzheimer's Disease, was taken first to the local hospital for assessment and then transferred to a residential home quite near where we lived. I was unhappy and very lonely to start with but within a few weeks, Joan was so much happier and relaxed that I realised that although I'd given her all the love and care I could, the stress of her condition had affected both of us."*

The feelings of loss are similar to bereavement in some ways. If you shared a bedroom you may find it hard to sleep. If you were used to being woken at night you may still have problems sleeping. If these continue and are affecting your ability to cope, see your GP.

The days may seem empty and long. You may find visits to the person you cared for an added strain. If their condition deteriorates this can be very distressing. If there is dementia the settling-down time, adjusting to new people, routines and surroundings may take some time. Sometimes, however, there may be a subtle change in roles.

*"When Gordon went into the nursing home he adapted much better than I did. He knew it was the best solution but I felt terrible, so guilty, as if I'd thrown him out. I almost lived at the home. I was there before breakfast each morning and would stay with him until he was settled for the night. After about three weeks, it was Gordon who convinced me that I didn't have to feel bad. He pointed out gently that I wasn't very good company as I never went anywhere or did anything. He suggested that I come once or twice a day for an hour or so but in the meantime did other things. Gradually I began to adapt to a different sort of life, one that wasn't centred on Gordon."*

Sometimes as a carer you may be tempted not to visit — it may be too painful or you may be angry or hurt. This is a good time to seek the support of friends and family if you have not done so before so that they can share the visiting.

It can also be hard to see care staff or nurses taking over. It can help to talk to the staff, to show an interest and encourage them to see the person as an individual with a complete background and not just another patient or resident. This is particularly important if the person is confused – telling staff what they were like before their dementia and what they did, makes a difference.

## IF YOU'RE WORRIED

If you feel the person you cared for is unhappy or that the care offered isn't appropriate, or even adequate, then you will want to do something. First talk to the owner or manager in charge of the home. Before you see them, take some time to look at what is happening and see if you can find a cause. For instance, is it due to staff, the way the home is run, the fact that the resident is being awkward? Express your concerns as calmly as possible.

If you find it hard to talk to the home owner, your social worker may be able to help. You could approach relatives of other residents for advice, or contact the Relatives Association which offers support and advice to relatives of people in care homes.

If all you get from the home is excuses and no action then you can go to the resident's doctor for extra support.

If this is still unsuccessful, contact the Registration Officer of the district health authority (for a nursing home) or the local authority (for a residential home.

# If you move away

You may have to stop caring because you're leaving the area. Often it will be possible to make arrangements before you go to ensure that the person you care for receives the right care. Certainly you'll want to tell social services of the change.

There may be several options. Some of the things you organise may be for your own peace of mind – like ensuring your relative or friend has a community alarm to be able to call for help in an emergency. Remember that needs may change so make whatever care you organise as flexible as possible.

*"When my husband was transferred up north it meant my 82-year-old mother would be living 250 miles away. I really worried about what would happen as she was determined not to move with us. At the time I felt angry. I thought I'd sit there worrying about her but she made the right decision. We got her a community alarm before*

*we left and had long chats with her GP and the health visitor. She has friends and neighbours who pop in, just as I did. When she began to have difficulty going upstairs we put in a stairlift. I made sure I knew the name of her social worker so when she had a knee operation recently I was able to organise extra care for her. I'm glad now she didn't move with us. She'd have had no social life and lost a lot of independence."*

## Fostering schemes

These schemes may be an alternative for an elderly person or for someone with special needs who doesn't want to go into residential care. Local families offer short-term respite care and sometimes long-term care with the person moving into the foster home to live as one of the family. Not all areas have these schemes. Ask social services if there's a 'Home from Home' scheme (or it may have another name) in your area.

## Coping with serious illness

If the person you care for is terminally ill you may need extra support at home. You may also want to think about hospice care or continuing care in hospital.

### HOSPICES
These offer patients with terminal illness, usually cancer, the care they need, usually for a short period of about ten days. There are over a hundred hospices in Britain and five hospices caring specifically for people with AIDS.

They're warm and welcoming places, certainly not places of despair. Most have a religious foundation but you don't have to be a practising member of any faith to be accepted. As most are independent there are no charges. Your GP will refer you.

**HOSPICE CARE AT HOME**

Through schemes such as Macmillan nurses and Marie Curie Cancer Care, it's possible for a trained nurse to come to your home to care for the patient. There's no charge and your GP will be able to organise it. In time the nurse can become a friend in whom you can confide. Mostly there will be one or two visits a day. Some hospices are now developing teams of trained volunteers who sit with patients overnight.

## Making a new life for yourself

You may have more time than you know what to do with. If you've been absorbed in caring this can be quite overwhelming. Carers who've devoted years of their lives often feel bitter when it's over and it's often easier to look back over the years rather than forward. It's especially hard for young carers who may miss out on a whole chunk of their youth (the Carers National Association has a section for young carers).

"I cared for my mum until I was in my 20s and then her multiple sclerosis got so bad she went into a home. That was seven years when I could have been out having fun. I felt resentful at the time but I felt worse when she'd gone. I did go for counselling and it did help. I can't have those years back but I do enjoy life now."

Older carers feel equally deprived – they are exhausted and often ill after years of caring. You may have led a very isolated existence and it is hard to go out into the world again. The answer is to start slowly and not feel guilty as you gradually find things to do to fill your days. You can feel proud of what you have achieved as a carer and use this knowledge as a springboard to a different life.

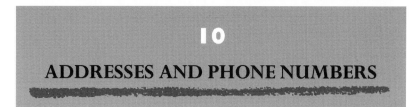

## SUPPORT AND INFORMATION

**Age Concern**
**England:** Astral House, 1268 London Road, London SW16 4ER
Tel: 081 679 8000
**Scotland:** 54a Fountainbridge, Edinburgh EH3 9PT
Tel: 031 228 5656
**Northern Ireland:** 3 Lower Crescent, Belfast BT7 1NR
Tel: 0232 245729
**Wales:** 4th Floor, 1 Cathedral Road, Cardiff CF1 9SD
Tel: 0222 371566
Provides advice, information and services for older people. Has useful factsheets – up to five can be applied for free. Most factsheets and booklets are available from local branches. You can also approach them for help with day and respite care.

**ASC (advice, advocacy and representation service for children and young people)**
Has a freephone number 0800 616101 every night weekdays 4pm – 10pm and at weekends 4pm – 8pm. At other times there is an answerphone – leave your name, address and phone number and say briefly what you need help with, if you can. A telephone counsellor will call back within 24 hours and pass you on to an advocate who will either visit you or advise you over the phone.

**Association of Crossroads Care Attendant Schemes**
10 Regent Place, Rugby, Warwickshire CV21 2PN
Tel: 0788 573653
Provides respite for carers. There are over 200 schemes throughout the UK – all are affiliated to the national association.

**The Boots Company Plc**
1 Thane Road West, Nottingham NG2 3AA
Tel: 0602 506 111

**British Association for Counselling**
1 Regent Place, Rugby, Warwickshire CV21 2PJ
Tel: 0788 578328

**British Holistic Medical Association**
179 Gloucester Place, London NW1 6DX
Tel: 071 262 5299
Has a tape on meditation and one which uses visualisation techniques for relaxation. You can leave a message on their 24 hour answerphone to receive details.

**British Humanist Association**
14 Lamb's Conduit Passage, London WC1R 4RH
Tel: 071 430 0908
Can provide information on non-religious funerals. Publishes *Funerals Without God* by Jane Wynne Willson (£3 including p&p) ISBN 090182514X.

**British Red Cross Society**
9 Grosvenor Crescent, London SW1X 7EJ
Tel: 071 235 5454
Has services for carers such as a Home from Hospital scheme, equipment loan and respite services.

**British Telecom**
Dial 150 and ask for disabled customers service.

**Care and Repair Ltd**
Castle House, Kirtley Drive, Nottingham NG7 LLD
Tel: 0602 799 091
A national co-ordinating body that advises on adapting homes.

**Carers National Association**
20/25 Glasshouse Yard, London EC1A 4JS
Tel: 071 490 8818 (Mon-Fri 1pm-4pm)

**Carers Line**
Tel: 071 490 8898

**Caring Costs**
Room 604, Charity Base, 50 Westminster Bridge Road, SE1 7QY
Tel: 071 721 7653
Campaigns for an independent income for carers.

**Charities Aid Foundation**
48 Pembury Road, Tonbridge, Kent TN9 2JD
Tel: 0732 771333
Publishes a Directory of Grant-Making Trusts. You can see a copy in your local library.

**Childline**
Royal Mail Building, Studd Street, London N1 0QW
Tel: Freefone 0800 11 11

**Council for Acupuncture**
179 Gloucester Place, London NW1 6DX
Tel: 071 724 5756

**Counsel and Care**
Twyman House, 16 Bonny Street, London NW1 9PG
Tel: 071 485 1566
Offers advice on accommodation and care for older people. Also has information on charitable grants.

**DIAL UK (Disablement, Information and Advice Line)**
Park Lodge, St. Catherine's Hospital, Tickhill Road, Balby, Doncaster, South Yorkshire, DN4 8QN
Tel: 0302 310 123

**Disability Information Service**
Roman House, 24 Greencoat Place, London SW1P 1DX
Tel: 071 630 5994

**Disability Information Trust**
Mary Marlborough Centre, Nuffield Orthopaedic Centre, Headington, Oxford OX3 7LD
Tel: 0865 227 592

**Disability Network UK**
8 Wolverhampton House, 123 Church Street, St Helens WA9 1JS
Tel: 0744 451 215

**Disabled Living Foundation**
380/384 Harrow Road, London W9 2HU
Tel: 071 289 6111
Has information about equipment that makes daily living easier and information about your nearest Disabled Living Centre.

**Family Welfare Association**
501-505 Kingsland Road, London E8 4AU
Tel: 071 254 6251
Provides grants and advice to those in need.

**Grey Agency Ltd**
PO Box 3054, London SW6 2HG
Tel: 071 736 3966
Has information on what is available for older people.

**Health Directory**
Tel: 0800 665544
For questions on health matters.
Tel: 0800 591220
For information on hospital waiting lists and times.

**Help the Aged**
4 St James's Walk, London EC1R 0BE
Tel: 071 253 0253 (Seniorline 0800 289404 Mon-Fri 10am-4pm)

**Homecraft Chestercare**
Low Moor Estate, Kirkby-in-Ashfield, North Yorkshire NG17 7JZ
Tel: 0623 757 955

**Hospice Information Service**
St Christopher's Hospice, 51-59 Lawrie Park Road, Sydenham, London SE26 6DZ
Tel: 081 778 9252

**Keep Able**
Fleming Close, Park Farm, Wellingborough, Northants NN8 6UF
Tel: 0933 679 426

**Nottingham Rehabilitation Ways and Means**
17 Ludlow Hill Road, West Bridgford, Nottingham NG2 6HD
Tel: 0602 452 345

**Relate**
National Marriage Guidance
Herbert Gray College, Little Church Street, Rugby CV21 3AP
Tel: 0788 573241

**Relatives Association**
5 Tavistock Place, London WC1H 9SS
Tel: 071 916 6055
Aims to put relatives of people in care homes in touch with one another.

**Royal College of Psychiatrists**
17 Belgrave Square, SW1X 8PG
Tel: 071 235 2351
Has a series of free leaflets on various aspects of depression that include information on tranquillisers
and anti-depressants.

**Samaritans**
10 The Grove, Slough, Bucks SL1 1QP
Tel: 0753 532 713
For your nearest branch and telephone number look in your local phone book.

**SPOD (Association to Aid the Sexual and Personal Relationships of People with a Disability)**
286 Camden Road, London N7 0BJ
Tel: 071 607 8851
Has information and advice on disability and sexuality and can put you in touch with a local counsellor.

**Terrence Higgins Trust**
52-54 Gray's Inn Road, London WC1X 8JU
Admin 10-5pm weekdays 071 831 0330
Legal line Weds 7-10pm: 071 405 2381
Helpline 3-10pm daily: 071 242 1010

**Westminster Pastoral Foundation**
23 Kensington Square, London W8 5HN
Tel: 071 937 6956

**Youth Access**
Magazine Business Centre, 11 Newark Street, Leicester LE1 5SS
Tel: 0533 558 763 (Mon to Fri 9am-5pm)
Can tell young people how to contact their nearest counsellor.

**ILLNESS AND DISABILITY**

**Alzheimer's Disease Society**
Gordon House, 10 Greencoat Place, London SW1 1PH
Tel: 071 306 0606

**Arthritis & Rheumatism Council (ARC)**
Copeman House, St Mary's Court, PO Box 177, St Mary's Gate, Chesterfield, Derby S41 7TD
Tel: 0246 558 033

**Arthritis Care**
18 Stephenson Way, London NW1 2HD (tel: 071 916 1500) Helpline Mon-Fri 12 noon to 4pm
Tel: 0800 289 170 (freephone)

**Bacup (British Association of Cancer United Patients)**
3 Bath Place, Rivington Street, EC2A 3JR
Tel: 071 613 2121 (freephone no. for callers outside 071 area: 0800 181 199; counselling service: 071 696 9000)
Offers a free, confidential cancer information service by phone and letter.

**British Acupuncture Association**
179 Gloucester Place, London NW1 6DX
Tel: 724 5756

**British Chiropractors Association**
29 Whitley Street, Reading, Berkshire RG2 0EG
Tel: 0734 757 557

**British Diabetic Association**
10 Queen Anne Street, London W1M 0BD
Tel: 071 323 1531

**British Epilepsy Association**
Anstey House, 40 Hanover Square, Leeds LS3 1BE
Tel: 0532 439 393 (helpline 0345 089 599)

**British Heart Foundation**
14 Fitzhardinge Street, London W1H 4DH
Tel: 071 935 0185

**Cancer Relief (Macmillan Fund)**
Anchor House, 15-19 Britten Street, London SW3 3TZ
Tel: 071 351 7811
Provides information about Macmillan nurses for cancer care.

**Cancerlink**
17 Britannia Street, London WC1X 9JN
Tel: 071 833 2451; 071 833 2818 (for information)
As well as offering support on all aspects of cancer, the organisation is a resource for local groups and can help set up new groups.

**Coloplast Advisory Service**
Freepost, Peterborough, Peterborough PE2 0BR
Tel: 0800 622 124
Has leaflets on incontinence and a freephone service will put you in touch with your nearest Continence Adviser.

**Continence Advisory Service**
Disability North, Castles Farm Road, Newcastle-upon-Tyne NE3 1PH
Tel: 091 213 0050 (Helpline is open weekdays 2pm-7pm)

**Continence Foundation**
2 Doughty Street, London WC1N 2PH
Tel: 071 404 6875

**General Council and Register of Osteopaths**
56 London Street, Reading, Berkshire RG1 4SQ
Tel: 0734 576 585

**Health Promotion Research Trust**
49-53 Regent Street, Cambridge CB2 1AB
Tel: 0223 69636
Has a useful leaflet on self-help for incontinence.

**Marie Curie Cancer Care**
28 Belgrave Square, London SW1X 8QG
Tel: 071 235 3325

**National Back Pain Association**
16 Elmtree Road, Teddington, Middlesex TW11 8ST
Tel: 081 977 5474
Provides information and leaflets on back problems, including a carer's guide to back care.

**Osteopath Medical Association**
22 Wimpole Street, London W1M 7AD
Tel: 071 323 4810

**Pain Concern**
PO Box 318, Canterbury, Kent CT4 5DP
Has a booklet on managing back pain. Enclose a 9"x6" sae with 28p stamp.

**Parkinsons Disease Society**
22 Upper Woburn Place, London WC1H 0RA
Tel: 071 383 3513

**Royal National Institute for Deaf People**
105 Gower Street, London WC1E 6AH
Tel: 071 387 8033 and 071 383 3154 minicom for the hard of hearing)

**Royal National Institute for the Blind (RNIB)**
224 Great Portland Street, London W1N 6AA
Tel: 071 388 1266

**RADAR (Royal Association for Disability and Rehabilitation)**
12 City Forum, 250 City Road, London EC1V 8AF
Tel:071 250 3222

**Society of Chiropodists**
53 Welbeck Street, London W1M 7HE
Tel: 071 486 3381

**Stroke Association**
CHSA House, Whitecross Street, London EC1Y 8JJ
Tel: 071 490 7999
Has useful books and leaflets and there are some local groups to offer support to stroke sufferers and their carers.

## LOSS AND BEREAVEMENT

**Cruse – Bereavement Care**
Cruse House, 126 Sheen Road, Richmond, Surrey TW9 1UR
Tel: 081 940 4818
Can offer bereavement counselling throughout Britain.

## BENEFITS AND FINANCE

**Benefits Agency**
Tel: 0345 227 722
Telephone advice line calls charged at local BT rates.

**Benefits Enquiry Line**
Freephone 0800 882 200 (weekdays 9am-4.30pm)

**Social Security Advice**
Freephone 0800 666 555 (weekdays 9am-4.30pm)
Social Security Office – in the phone book under Social Security or Benefits Agency

## HOUSING

**Abbeyfield Society**
186-192 Darkes Lane, Potters Bar, Herts EN6 1AB
Tel: 0707 644845
Offers sheltered housing for rent in adapted family houses. Some have a resident housekeeper, others offer round-the-clock care.

**Anchor**
Anchor House, 269a Banbury Road, Oxford OX2 7HU
Tel: 0865 311 511
Can offer advice on Staying Put schemes and provides sheltered and very sheltered accommodation.

**British Federation of Care Home Proprietors**
852 Melton Road, Thurmaston, Leicester LE4 8BN
Tel: 0533 640 095

**Elderly Accommodation Counsel**
46a Chiswick High Road, London W4 1SZ
Tel: 081 742 1182
Has information on residential and nursing homes for elderly people, including those which accept people suffering from dementia.

## ALCOHOL

**Alcohol Concern**
275 Grays Inn Road, London WC1X 8QF
Tel: 071 833 3471

**Alcoholics Anonymous**
11 Redcliffe Gardens, London SW10 9BG
Tel: 071 352 3001
or
PO Box 1, Stonebow House, Stonebow, York YO1 2NJ

**Alcoholics Anonymous Family Groups**
61 Great Dover Street, London SE1 4YF
Tel: 071 403 0888

## SMOKING

**Ash – Action on Smoking and Health**
101 Gloucester Place, London W1H 3PH
Tel: 071 935 3519

**Quit**
102 Gloucester Place, London W1H 3DA
Smoker's quit line 071 487 3000

## TRANQUILLISERS

**Council for Involuntary Tranquilliser Addiction, CITA**
Cavendish House, Brighton Road, Waterloo, Liverpool L22 5NG
Has a tape on coping with anxiety. Send a cheque for £6.75 payable to CITA.

## FREE TIME

**British Correspondence Chess Association**
86 Mortimer Road, London N1 4LH
Tel: 071 254 7912
Organises postal chess for all levels.

**Conversation by Correspondence Through Friends by Post (Friends by Post)**
6 Bollin Court, Macclesfield Road, Wilmslow, Cheshire SK9 2AP
Links people of all backgrounds and ages by finding them someone to write to. Please enclose sae.

**Holiday Care Service**
2 Old Bank Chambers, Station Road, Horley, Surrey RH6 9HW
Tel: 0293 774 535

**Horticultural Therapy**
Goulds Ground, Vallis Way, Frome, Somerset BA11 4BB
Tel: 0373 464782
Aims to help older and disabled people so that they can continue to enjoy gardening.

**National Retreat Association**
Liddon House, 24 South Audley Street, London W1Y 5DL
Tel: 071 493 3534
Has an information service and publishes *The Vision* which gives a list of houses offering accommodation and a calendar of retreat events.

**National Extension College**
18 Brooklands Avenue, Cambridge CB2 2HN
Tel: 0223 316 644

**Open University**
Central Enquiry Service
PO Box 200, Milton Keynes MK7 6AG
Provides information about courses in arts, computing, science, community interests.

**Relaxation for Living**
Mrs Amber Lloyd, 168-170 Oatlands Drive, Weybridge, Surrey KT13 9ET
Tel: 0932 831 000

**Shape**
Chair, Shape Network, c/o East Midlands Shape, 27a Belvoir Street, Leicester LE1 6FL (for nearest service)
Involves elderly and disabled people in the arts.

**Sports Council**
16 Upper Woburn Place, London WC1H 0QP
Tel: 071 388 1277

**Talking Newspaper Association (TNAUK)**
90 High Street, Heathfield, East Sussex TN21 8DB
Tel: 0435 866 102
Produces tapes of local newspapers, 100 national newspapers and magazines. Guide to Tape Services for the Handicapped costs £5 including p&p.

**Transcendental Meditation (TM)**
This is another form of meditation which helps many people feel less stressed. Write to TM, Freepost, Lancashire, WN8 6BR, or telephone freephone 0800 269303 for information on your nearest TM centre.

**Tripscope**
Pamwell House, 160 Pennywell Road, Bristol, Avon BS5 0TX
Tel: Bristol: 0272 414094/London: 081 994 9294
Provides an information service on travel and transport for people with mobility problems wherever they live and wherever they want to travel. The service is free to elderly and disabled people and to their carers.

**Winged Fellowship Trust**
Angel House, 20-32 Pentonville Road, London N1 9XD
Tel: 071 833 2594
Offers holidays and respite for the severely physically disabled at home and abroad.

**WRVS**
234-244 Stockwell Road, London SW9 9SP
Tel: 071 416 0146